THE

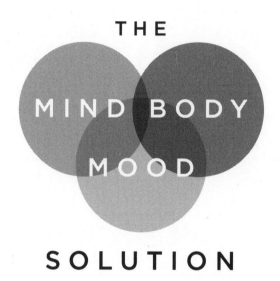

MIND BODY

MOOD

SOLUTION

THE

MIND BODY

MOOD

SOLUTION

The Breakthrough Drug-Free Program
for Lasting Relief from Depression

Jeffrey Rossman, PhD

RODALE

To my parents, Anita and Herb, *my first, best teachers*

To Diane, *whose love lights my life*

And to Grace and Gabriel, *my joy and inspiration*

© 2011 by Jeffrey Rossman, PhD

Direct and trade hardcover editions published simultaneously in January 2011.

Printed in the United States of America

Rodale Inc. makes every effort to use acid-free ∞, recycled paper ♻.

Book design by Joanna Williams

Library of Congress Cataloging-in-Publication Data

Rossman, Jeffrey.
   The mind-body mood solution : the breakthrough program for overcoming depression rapidly, naturally, and permanently / Jeffrey Rossman.
      p.   cm.
   Includes bibliographical references and index.
   ISBN 978-1-60961-043-2   Direct hardcover
   ISBN 978-1-60529-570-1   Trade hardcover
   1. Depression, Mental—Alternative treatment.   2. Mind and body therapies.
   I. Title.
RC537.R653   2011
616.85'27—dc22   2010042937

2   4   6   8   10   9   7   5   3   1 hardcover

RODALE
LIVE YOUR WHOLE LIFE™

We inspire and enable people to improve their lives and the world around them.

For more of our products visit **rodalestore.com** or call 800-848-4735.

CONTENTS

PROLOGUE

If you are struggling with feelings of depression now or have experienced bouts of depression in the past, I'm very glad that you've found this book. *The Mind-Body Mood Solution* offers a powerful set of tools that can help you lift your mood and positively transform your life.

While you may experience significant improvements right away, the techniques I will share in the coming pages do not offer a quick fix, nor are they a magic pill. You will need to make lifestyle changes and practice skills that will increase your self-awareness, get your energy moving, and lift your mood. If you commit yourself to these processes, they will not only help you feel better now, they will also help you stay physically and emotionally healthy for years to come.

The techniques I offer in *The Mind-Body Mood Solution* are strategies I've found to be successful for hundreds of my patients over the past 20 years. I realize that it can be challenging to apply the principles and tools printed on a book page to your own life; I wish that we could sit together so that I could help you through this process in person. However, in this book you will find the same tools and practices I share with my clients. I will guide you through the process of lifting your mood and ask you many of the same questions I pose to them. Because each person is unique and no one experiences the symptoms of depression in the same way, you will be able to customize your program by using the resources that are most useful to you.

If you are experiencing significant depression now, I suggest you ask for support from someone you trust. This could be a friend, a family member, a therapist, or a coach. Turn to Chapter 14 for specific advice on finding a therapist when professional help is needed.

Although the prevalence of depression is growing dramatically, most cases go untreated. Only one in three individuals suffering from depression receives treatment. There is still a stigma that prevents many people from seeking help for mental health issues. My hope is that we can move beyond the barriers created by that stigma so that everyone who is suffering can be helped. The earlier depression is treated, the more effectively and rapidly recovery can be achieved.

Fortunately, we have developed very effective treatments over the past 2 decades. Several types of psychotherapy have proven to be particularly helpful in relieving depression. Physical approaches involving nutrition, exercise, and exposure to bright light have also demonstrated a powerful, positive effect on depression. I have found that combining interventions that address both the mind *and* the body helps my clients recover more rapidly and durably than utilizing any one approach in isolation. I have been fortunate over the past 18 years to work at Canyon Ranch, a health resort and integrative wellness center in the Berkshire Mountains of western Massachusetts. In this setting, my clients are able to utilize complementary approaches including exercise, breathing, meditation, and nutrition. Very often, these approaches yield rapid results.

How to Use the Book and the Program

As you read through the opening chapters of this book, give some thought to whether these treatment options feel right for you and how much time you think you'll be able to devote to them. Also, be sure to complete the Readiness Assessment on page 13 to learn how you can get the most out of the program.

As you embark on this program, you may find it helpful to review and assess your progress periodically. To get a baseline measure of how you're feeling now, you can complete the depression assessment test (CES-D) on page 21. I suggest you retake this assessment each week for the next 8 weeks. Benchmarking your progress as you follow the program will help you evaluate its effectiveness.

The program offers several tools that you can use on a daily basis to enhance your mood. Some of these may be more helpful to you than others. Try them out and see what works best for you. The

Readiness Assessment quiz will help you determine which strategies may be most useful for you and which tools you're most inclined to use. For instance, if your low mood is heavily related to nutritional deficiencies or dietary sensitivities, you may find the nutritional component of the program to be very effective. If your unhappiness is more influenced by a negative thought pattern, the attitudinal component may be most helpful to you. Chances are you will find that a combination of treatments is most relevant and useful for you.

Transforming Energy

At the heart of the program is the understanding that when we are feeling depressed, our life energy is blocked and we have difficulty moving forward. Life energy is the energy that is present in all living things, including plants, animals, and human beings. It is the energy that powers all the systems of your body and gives you a feeling of vitality. Each component of this program is designed to help you unblock your energy so that it flows naturally.

The energy blockage in depression is evident in several ways. Physically, most depressed people experience fatigue and lethargy. It is often difficult to get moving and find the energy to accomplish what you need to do each day. Others experience agitation and restlessness, and find that the energy they do have is stuck in a negative, uncomfortable pattern.

Emotionally, depression blunts life energy. The heaviness of depression weighs down our emotional life with feelings of guilt, despair, fear, regret, and resentment. Some people simply feel numb. The absence of emotion robs them of any joy or pleasure in life. Their emotions and their energy are stuck in a constricted pattern, rather than flowing outward toward others in positive expressions of love, appreciation, and engagement.

Energy blockage is also evident in the impaired cognitive functioning experienced by many people with depression. Problems with attention and memory are very common. Depressed students have trouble concentrating on their studies, depressed workers have trouble completing tasks, and depressed parents have trouble engaging with their children. For many, the endless cycle of replaying ruminative thoughts keeps their energy stuck in a circuit that prevents constructive, creative thinking. Unwanted rumination also hijacks the mind at night and interferes with sleep patterns.

When our physical, emotional, and cognitive energy is stuck, we find it impossible to move forward. We withdraw from friends and family, and hold back from initiating new projects, travel, or any other enterprise that requires our full emotional and physical engagement. We sometimes use unhealthy methods of avoiding or numbing our feelings, such as overindulging in alcohol, food, television, or sleep. This avoidant behavior is at the heart of depression.

Using the Program

The Mind-Body Mood Solution is designed to work with your body and your mind simultaneously to unblock your energy and get it moving in a positive direction. Each component of the program addresses a vital source of energy. Here is a brief overview of the physical strategies you will find in this book to help you accomplish this goal.

Nutrition: You will learn ways of eating that enhance your mood by balancing your blood sugar, hormones, and brain chemistry. In addition, you will receive information about vitamins and supplements that support your physical and emotional well-being.

Exercise: You will learn about the powerful mood-boosting effects of physical exercise: increases in cerebral bloodflow, neurotransmitter production, new brain cells, and new neural pathways. Exercise literally transforms your brain, producing an ongoing feeling of well-being and strengthening your capacity to handle stress.

Sleep Enhancement: You will learn strategies for improving the quality of your sleep and giving your body the rest it needs to replenish your energy and refresh your mood.

Bright Light: You will learn how exposure to sunlight and high-intensity light fixtures can boost your mood and improve your sleep.

Breathing Practices: You will be introduced to a variety of breathing techniques that will calm, balance, and enhance your life energy. These techniques enable you to be more focused and alert, and to tap into a calm, clear state of awareness.

Other components of the program will help you unblock your energy through mental strategies and exercises. During the past 25 years, I have integrated several approaches to emotional healing into the program presented in this book. A number of the psychological principles and techniques I offer are drawn from a system of healing and personal development known as psychosynthesis, which embraces the spiritual dimension of human experience. Psychosynthesis is designed to help individuals become more self aware and able to direct their actions in accordance with their core values. Other components of this program are drawn from the fields of mindfulness, cognitive-behavioral therapy, and positive psychology. These strategies include:

The Practice of Presence: Living in the present helps you connect with a rich source of vitality. It also helps you become aware of your thought processes and allows you to observe your thoughts compassionately, without being ruled by them.

Overcoming Avoidance: Choosing to experience rather than avoid potentially uncomfortable situations and emotions is another source of vitality that is a key to overcoming depression. You will identify what you have been avoiding and learn strategies for overcoming avoidance.

Techniques for Transforming Judgment: These techniques will help you identify and transform negative thought patterns and cultivate positive attitudes that dissolve depression and enhance feelings of well-being.

Forgiveness and Gratitude: Our attitude toward what we experience has a powerful effect on our mood. By cultivating an attitude of forgiveness toward ourselves and others, we free our emotional energy from toxic anger, resentment, shame, and guilt. Choosing to be grateful for what we have and for kindness received is also a powerful antidote to depression.

The Power of Action: It's crucial to plan for and engage in activities that give you feelings of pleasure and accomplishment. Constructive activity helps support and channel your life energy.

The Courage to Change What You Can: Connecting with your core values enables you to tap into a powerful source of vitality and helps you address and change the areas of your life that are not working.

Resilience Strategies: These techniques will help you face significant life challenges by fortifying your capacity to deal with trauma, loss, and transition.

As you actively engage in the program and your energy becomes unblocked, you will feel yourself gradually becoming more awake and alive. You will develop a greater awareness of what your body needs to function at its peak. You will learn optimal ways of eating, moving, breathing, and sleeping that will give you the raw materials and catalysts to boost your energy and keep it flowing smoothly.

You will also gain a deeper understanding of how your mind works and how to make it your ally in living a vital, satisfying life. Through the awareness practices, you will become more fully awake to life as it is unfolding moment by moment. You will learn what weighs down your mood and what lifts it, and how to release what you are ready to change or let go of. You will learn to recognize negative thoughts that contribute to depression, and how to access a more constructive thought process. You will learn powerful techniques for strengthening your connection with the wise, compassionate part of your mind that is able to observe your thoughts, feelings, and sensations without becoming caught up in them. From this place you can respond thoughtfully rather than react reflexively to stressful events. Cultivating this awareness is the key to genuine freedom and self-acceptance, regardless of the obstacles you confront in life.

Techniques for transforming judgment enable you to change limiting, conditioned patterns of thinking and feeling. As you transform judgment, you release yourself from the toxic grip of anger, resentment, shame, guilt, and frustration. Emotional blocks dissolve, and your energy is freed to flow into positive emotions and actions. You become more accepting of yourself and compassionate toward others. In the later chapters of the book, we will explore how this approach can be used to deal with life-altering events.

In the chapters that follow, you will find effective practices that you can begin to use today. They work more powerfully in combination than alone, and you can design your own program from the wide menu of mental and physical strategies mentioned above.

The skills and practices you will learn will do more than help you overcome depression: They will enhance your health and well-being for the rest of your life.

My Connection with Depression

My connection with depression is deeply personal. When I was 7 years old, my maternal grandmother came to live with my family. She was a warm and fun-loving companion who loved me wholeheartedly.

She had just been discharged from the hospital after one of her many bouts of clinical depression. She had endured several hospitalizations and electroshock treatments, which impaired her memory and weakened her heart.

I remember the times when she struggled to catch her breath. Sometimes she would grab my arm and ask me to find the bottle of nitroglycerin tablets in her purse and bring it to her. In the middle of the night on September 24, 1960, she awoke gasping for air. My mother called my grandmother's doctor, who got lost trying to find our house. By the time he finally arrived, it was too late. My grandmother had passed away. Filled with sadness and confusion, I struggled to understand what had happened.

Depression was a frequent visitor in our family. My mother's father had also suffered from clinical depression in the latter part of his life. He was a hard-edged man, whose sharp, critical personality made him a tough customer. He became severely depressed late in his life, and at one point, he and my grandmother were hospitalized for depression in the same hospital. I can barely imagine my mother's anguish, tending to her parents in the hospital while working as a schoolteacher and raising two small children. Both of my maternal grandparents died of heart attacks, she at 60, he at 62, their lives shortened by heavy smoking, a sedentary lifestyle, and the cardiovascular damage caused by chronic depression.

My father's mother also suffered bouts of clinical depression. She was hospitalized with clinical depression when her husband, my grandfather, sold their corner grocery store and started a new venture with a business partner. She was consumed with fear that the partnership would not work out and the family would become penniless and homeless. My grandfather managed to make the transition successfully, but my grandmother spent a week in the hospital. After seeing that the business wasn't going to fail, she eventually made a full recovery.

Seeing my grandparents live with depression left a deep and lasting impression on me. I saw how profoundly they suffered, and I wanted to know why. My parents did their best to explain, but I was left wondering how my grandparents could have become so discouraged and hopeless. Most of all, I wished I could have done something to help them.

I also saw how much my parents' lives were impacted by their parents' depression. I saw their pain and helplessness when my father's mother was hospitalized again for depression later in her life. She became despondent after suffering broken ribs in a fall. She gave up her will to live and passed away within a year.

My maternal grandmother's long-standing depression had a profound impact on my mother. From the time she was 8 years old, my mother cared for herself, her younger brother, and at times her own mother. She learned at a young age that life could be harsh and she would need to rely on herself. She did well in school, put herself through college with her wages from working for the post office, and became a high school teacher. She was blessed with resilience, and she faced the challenge of her mother's condition with compassion and a sense of responsibility. That is not to say she never became angry or frustrated with my grandmother, because she did. But regardless of her frustration and at times embarrassment, she never stopped taking care of her mother.

As a teenager I felt a desire to understand and help people who were suffering like my grandparents had. During my freshman year in college, I volunteered in a psychiatric hospital, providing support to patients and their families. Throughout my time in college and in the years immediately following my graduation, I worked in a number of psychiatric hospitals with depressed, suicidal, and psychotic patients. My job was to protect them from harming themselves or others and to support them in becoming well enough to go home. I felt encouraged by seeing many people make excellent recoveries and by being part of the team that helped them get better.

In these hospitals the primary therapeutic modalities were medication, psychotherapy, and group therapy. For those severely depressed patients whose condition did not respond to medication or talk therapy, electroconvulsive therapy was used with remarkable efficacy. Unfortunately, many patients also suffered permanent memory loss as a result of the treatment. I accompanied some of these patients to their ECT treatments, assisted during the procedure, and reassured them when they regained consciousness. I wheeled them back to their rooms and consoled them when they awoke from the anesthesia, frightened and disoriented. Over time, as they emerged from the dark shadow of depression, I helped them prepare to return to their lives at home.

As I sat with these patients, I thought about my grandmother and the shock treatments she received, her fear and confusion, and her unending cycle of depression, recovery, and relapse. I wondered how her life might have been different if, early on, she had learned effective ways to care for herself and her mood. I became interested in helping people overcome and stay free of depression.

At one of these hospitals, I worked the night shift 1 week out of every 3. I'd drive home at 7:30 in the morning after working all night, checking in on patients who were in many cases psychotic, suicidal, or violent. I'd fall into bed exhausted, but I never managed to sleep soundly during the day. I felt continually out of sync with the rest of the world and with my body. Even when I worked a normal daytime shift, I couldn't get into a regular sleep routine. Over time, the experience of rotating between shifts and sleeping poorly took a devastating toll on my mood. I was perpetually tired, depressed, and frustrated with myself. While my experience working in this hospital helped me to understand and respond to suffering, it also brought me to a dark, low place in my own life.

During this period between college and graduate school, I searched for ways to heal myself. I discovered that a diet of wholesome, nutritious foods improved my energy and clarity. I reconnected with my lifelong love of exercise, getting into a regular jogging routine, playing racquetball, and joining a soccer team. I worked with a therapist and developed a greater awareness of my emotions and inner life. I explored what I wanted to do with my life and how to take steps to move forward. I learned to meditate, which provided relief from feelings of anxiety and depression. Meditation gave me a powerful experience of a deeper, wiser place within myself from which I could observe my thoughts and my feelings without being trapped in them. The practice and the philosophy around it opened up a new world for me. I went on several meditation and yoga retreats that helped me deepen my practice and understanding. All of the changes I made through therapy, diet, exercise, and meditation helped me to feel more energetic and whole. I learned that a mind-body approach was an effective way to overcome my own depression. In the spring of 1978, I made plans to attend graduate school, and I met my future wife.

That fall I entered graduate school at Adelphi University in Long Island, New York. In my graduate training and my internship at Harvard Medical School's Department of Psychiatry at the Massachusetts Mental Health Center, the prevailing treatment paradigm was psychodynamic. We focused on identifying each patient's areas of dysfunction and helped them understand and work through the past issues that contributed to their current difficulties. The training helped me to understand the ways in which early relationships and experiences influence personality development and emotional health.

In the late 1980s and early 1990s, I directed behavioral health services at an outpatient holistic health center. Our staff included physicians, nutritionists, exercise specialists, acupuncturists, and massage therapists. Our patients came for treatment of conditions such as cancer, AIDS, chronic fatigue syndrome, autoimmune conditions, diabetes, and heart disease. Many of our patients also suffered from depression, either as their primary reason for seeking help or in conjunction with a coexisting medical condition. Seeing my clients recover from depression rapidly and durably using an integrated mind-body approach convinced me of its power and effectiveness.

At Canyon Ranch, where I have been directing the Life Management Department since 1993, our integrative mind-body approach has helped thousands of people overcome depression. In the process, they have developed lifestyle practices that continue to support their overall health. Guests at Canyon Ranch often feel remarkably better within days of starting treatment because of their immediate immersion in a healthy lifestyle. From the day they arrive, they eat nutritious meals, engage in different types of exercise, and practice breathing and meditative techniques. Many guests take part in outdoor activities such as tai chi, kayaking, a morning walk, or a vigorous hike in the mountains. They participate in a full schedule of mood-enhancing activities and devote all their attention to their health and well-being.

Guests at Canyon Ranch also have the opportunity to work with a variety of health practitioners who share a holistic, mind-body-spirit approach to health care. Our doctors, nurses, nutritionists, acupuncturists, psychotherapists, energy healers, exercise physiologists, and bodyworkers communicate with one another to help our guests develop an integrated plan for lifestyle change. For example, a guest I work with might also have an evaluation with a physician, a nutritionist, and an exercise physiologist. With the guest's permission, we consult with one another to provide recommendations that integrate the insights from our various disciplines.

I realize it is more challenging to implement the strategies in this program when you are not staying at a health resort. However, if you are willing to devote some time to the practices, they are extremely doable at home. In fact, I use a similar approach with individuals in my private practice. Many of the case histories in this book are the stories of my clients who engaged with the program on their own. Some of them worked with personal trainers, nutritionists, or acupuncturists in addition to their work with me. In some cases, I referred them to a physician to be evaluated for medical conditions that could be contributing to their depression.

Some of the people I work with have experienced depressed feelings in response to a traumatic life event. Others have experienced low-grade depression throughout most of their lives. All of the people whose stories you will read have chosen to take charge of their mood and their health. I hope that you, too, will be interested in learning how to enhance your mood and take steps toward living a vital, fulfilling life.

INTRODUCTION

A New Way to Understand Depression

We are living in an age of depression. Despite extraordinary advances in our standard of living, rates of depression have sky-rocketed in the past 50 years. Depression is 10 times more prevalent today than in 1960, and the rate of depression is doubling every 10 years. Depression is the leading cause of disability in the United States. Approximately 25 percent of Americans will experience severe, clinical depression at some point in their lives. The annual cost of treating these patients is $26 billion. At any given time, approximately one out of four Americans reports being at least mildly depressed. One in eight women is taking an antidepressant. Use of these drugs is so common, in fact, that in many of America's cities and towns, traces of antidepressants can be found in the water supply.

The incidence of depression is also increasing dramatically in other industrialized countries, including Australia, Great Britain, Germany, and South Korea. Rates of depression are much lower in developing countries, but they are rising slowly there, too, as these nations become Westernized. It is estimated by the World Health Organization that by 2050, depression will be the leading cause of disability in the world.

What is causing this staggering epidemic of depression? How can we understand the rise in depression in a nation as privileged as the United States? We have access to conveniences and luxuries that our grandparents and great-grandparents could scarcely have dreamed of. We have the ability to travel long distances at high speeds, access to an abundance of cheap food, exposure to television with hundreds of channels available 24 hours a day, the luxury of climate-controlled cars and work spaces, and the freedom to live virtually anywhere. At the push of a button we can cook our food, wash our clothes, and be entertained as we sit on our couches. So why is it that, in spite of these comforts, more people are depressed than ever before?

The truth is, more Americans are becoming depressed *because* of these conveniences. Sweeping cultural changes in the way we live, work, travel, eat, sleep, play, and relate to one another have made us increasingly vulnerable to depression. We are living out of sync with nature, our bodies, our spirits, and each other—and we are paying a hefty price for it.

To understand why our modern lifestyle makes us especially susceptible to depression, we need to take a closer look at our origins. The bodies we inhabit today evolved hundreds of thousands of years ago in a very different environment. For our caveman ancestors, food was scarce and predators were plentiful. In order to gather enough food to be nourished, they spent the majority of their time hunting and foraging. They walked many miles a day and lifted heavy objects, carrying water and other supplies for survival. They spent their days outdoors, engaged in physical labor with other members of their clan. Living in harmony with the rising and setting of the sun, their biological rhythms evolved in concert with the rhythms of nature.

With the advent of agriculture, humans continued to live in harmony with nature, engaging in strenuous physical activity and spending most of their time outdoors. When the sun went down, they went to sleep, and when the sun came up, they awoke. Families and communities worked together to raise the crops and animals they depended on for survival. Humans evolved as social creatures in highly interdependent social groups.

Our bodies and brains were never designed for the conditions in which we find ourselves today. In modern American society, most of us work indoors at jobs that require little physical labor. We spend more of our time working than any other culture in the world. We eat refined foods loaded with chemicals and artificial ingredients. We sleep an hour less on average than we did just 50 years ago.

Many of us live apart from our families and the communities in which we were raised. In the past 25 years, shared family dinners and family vacations have decreased by more than one-third, and the popularity of having friends over to visit has decreased by 25 percent. We can isolate ourselves from our neighbors in houses that are twice as big as they were just two generations ago, even though families are smaller. Alone in our giant houses, we spend much of our leisure time staring idly at electronic screens. In fact, in 2009 teenagers spent an average of 7 to 8 hours a day (that's almost every waking nonschool hour) connected to some kind of electronic device, whether it was a TV, computer, handheld video game, cell phone, or iPod. We spend far less time engaged with others in community and family life than did our parents' generation. In the past 25 years, participation in clubs and civic organizations has decreased by 50 percent.

We also live in a culture that is highly focused on mental tasks. Our televisions, radios, computers, and BlackBerries bombard us with a constant stream of urgent messages. Our public education system trains us for a life of mental engagement. Children are taught how to read, write, and use computers, not how to plant vegetables or recognize deer tracks. They learn the needed skills to become office workers. We have become a nation that lives from the neck up, from behind a desk or a counter, and for many of us the incessant stream of mental chatter rarely stops.

Modern American life has also become disconnected from spirituality. For most cultures throughout history, the world was animated with spirit. Although many Americans today claim a religious affiliation, church attendance has decreased by about one-third since the 1960s. Interestingly, there is one cultural group in America for whom depression is virtually nonexistent: the Amish. When I was a child growing up in eastern Pennsylvania, we would occasionally drive into Amish country, where it wasn't unusual to see a family dressed modestly in simple black clothing, riding down the street in a horse and buggy. When I learned that the Amish did not have cars, televisions, or other modern conveniences, I remember feeling sorry for them. Little did I know that their traditional way of life allows them to be more resilient and content than those of us who drive by them in our automobiles. Working with their hands, living close to nature, embracing the spiritual, and prioritizing the common good of the community have all helped the Amish remain relatively immune to depression. If you have ever witnessed a barn-raising firsthand, you are familiar with the physical vitality and communal spirit that make this group uniquely resilient.

Depression also takes a serious toll on our physical health. Being depressed increases the risk of many diseases, including heart disease, cancer, and cognitive impairment. The rise in depression has paralleled our nation's increase in both obesity and sleep deprivation over the past half century. In the past decade we have begun to understand the ill effects of the modern American diet, which has played a large part in the current epidemics of obesity and type 2 diabetes. Diet also plays a role in depression.

We are slowly beginning to realize that living out of harmony with our own nature contributes to the depression epidemic. Genuine and lasting recovery requires realignment with what is natural and nourishing to our lives. *The Mind-Body Mood Solution* will enable you to overcome depression by discovering how to live in harmony with your body, mind, and spirit.

What about Medication?

There are many paths to depression. Some people carry a genetic susceptibility. Others become depressed in response to nutritional deficiencies, physical illness, sleep deprivation, trauma, loss, or a combination of these factors. Others engage in habitual patterns of negative thinking or avoidant behavior that contribute to depression.

Over the past several years, depression has increasingly come to be viewed as a biological illness. The disease model of depression sees it as a brain disorder marked by changes in brain function. In clinical depression, there are indeed changes in brain function and structure observable with neuroimaging; these include decreased activity in the left prefrontal cortex and decreased cell volume in the hippocampus. Depressed people also tend to have higher levels of cortisol, a stress hormone provided by the adrenal gland, as well as inflammation.

While the physiological changes that accompany severe depression support the disease model, it is neither the only nor the most productive way of understanding depression. The disease model conveys the idea that depression is something that you "catch," like a cold or the flu. One problem with this definition is that it suggests that depression is a biological condition outside of your control—something that, like other diseases, can be fixed with the right medication. If your depression is mild to moderate, this way of understanding depression can be disempowering and may keep you from pursuing more active steps to improve your life and your mood.

I believe in looking at depression as a signal from your body and mind that something in your life is out of balance and needs to change. It may be that you're getting inadequate nutrition or not enough sleep or exercise. Or perhaps it's an indication that change is needed in a close relationship, your career, or another important area of your life. It may be that you are simply trapped in old, constricted ways of thinking that are blocking your energy.

When you view depression as a signal that something needs to change, it puts the power to make that change in your hands. You can learn to nourish yourself with food and supplements that boost your energy, you can start an exercise program that brightens your mood, you can think in fresh new ways that liberate your spirit. You can make a change in an important relationship or your career, or come to terms with a loss or disappointment. From this perspective, depression is not so much a disorder to be treated as it is a call to awaken to the possibility of living a vital and fulfilling life.

It is unfortunate that so much of the discussion about depression is centered on the idea that it results from an imbalance in brain chemistry—a problem we can solve by taking a pill. The pharmaceutical industry, in particular, has done a masterful job of promoting this belief. With diagrams of neurons and neurotransmitters illuminated on your television screen, they make a compelling scientific pitch: You have a chemical imbalance in your brain, and the best way for you to become well is to take a drug to balance your neurotransmitters. Although depression often does involve neurotransmitter imbalances, there are many other ways to change neurotransmitter levels and affect brain function, including the lifestyle modifications provided in this book.

One of the most recognizable symptoms of depression is an unquiet mind: the mind that judges you, prods you, and awakens you from desperately needed sleep at 3:00 a.m. If you were to believe the commercials you see in between segments of the evening news, you would think that the solution for this early-morning awakening is a sleeping pill or a daily regimen of an antidepressant. "Can't get your mind to turn off? You need Drug X to quiet your busy mind." "Feeling down? You need Drug Y to boost your serotonin level." Is it coincidental that these ads for mood-enhancing drugs are interspersed with ominous news reports of war, natural disasters, violent crimes, and economic turmoil? The timing of these commercials works brilliantly. More and more people are asking their doctors for the drugs they see advertised.

Pharmaceutical companies' skillfully delivered messages are extraordinarily successful. In the United States, 10 million people are taking antidepressants, at a cost of $11.9 billion in 2007. In that same year, more prescriptions for antidepressants—232.7 million—were written than for any other class of drug. Between 1996 and 2005, the number of people taking antidepressants doubled. During that same period, direct-to-consumer advertising (i.e., the drug commercials on TV and the ads in magazines) of antidepressants quadrupled.

Three major factors have influenced the dramatic rise in anti-depressant use over the past 15 years: (1) the development of a new class of drugs, SSRIs, which have fewer initial side effects than previous generations of antidepressants; (2) legislation that reversed the ban on direct marketing of drugs to consumers; and (3) the reduction in medical insurance coverage for psychotherapy available through HMOs. As fewer people turn to psychotherapy for help with depression, more people turn to drugs. This is unfortunate, because psychotherapy has been shown to relieve depression at least as quickly and effectively as medication, with one important difference: Fewer patients who undergo psycho-therapy experience a recurrence of depression.

A large-scale study conducted by the National Institute of Mental Health (NIMH) and published in 2006 in the *American Journal of Psychiatry* looked at depressed patients who received follow-up treatment after deriving no benefit from a course of treatment with the antidepressant Celexa. After their unproduc-tive treatment with Celexa, they were given either one of three additional antidepressants or a course of cognitive therapy. The patients who received cognitive therapy were significantly more likely to achieve complete remission than the patients who were given medication. An earlier, multiyear, multicenter NIMH study found no difference in overall effects between patients treated with the antidepressant Tofranil and those who underwent brief trials of both cognitive and interpersonal therapy. However, after 18 months the patients in the cognitive and interpersonal therapy groups were functioning better (though not at a statistically significant level) than those in the medication group.

There is also evidence that therapy may produce results more quickly than medication does. A study published in 2005 found that patients receiving cognitive-behavioral therapy recovered from clinical depression more rapidly than those receiving antidepressants. And a study published in 2006 in the *Journal of Neuropsychopharmacology* found that cognitive-behavioral therapy was significantly better than medication in preventing future episodes of depression. While both therapy and medication have been shown in recent studies to produce changes in brain function, the changes wrought by psychotherapy, which are accompanied by genuine learning, tend to be more enduring. The same is true for aerobic exercise as a means of treating depression. Patients who participate in both exercise and therapy learn how to engage in ways of living that keep them healthy and in balance over the long term.

But if psychotherapy and exercise are more effective than medication in treating and preventing a relapse of depression, why is a depressed patient more likely to leave his or her doctor's office with a prescription for Prozac than a referral for psychotherapy or a recommendation to join a gym? The forces that influence doctors to prescribe drugs are deeply embedded in the economics and psychology of our health care industry. Insurance company reimbursement policies put increasing pressure on primary care physicians to see as many patients as possible in as little time as possible. Writing a prescription is an expedient way to treat a depressed patient who may be experiencing a complicated reaction to a loss, conflict, or trauma. Psychiatrists are also incentivized to prescribe medication by higher reimbursement rates for medication visits than for psychotherapy sessions. Health insurance companies favor medication over psychotherapy because pills are cheaper than office visits.

Over the past 2 decades, health insurers have implemented policies that make it difficult for their subscribers to receive reimbursement for therapy. Some HMOs maintain stringent limits on the number of visits they will reimburse, and many require voluminous documentation from the health care provider before they will authorize additional sessions. These policies constitute a burden to providers and a significant threat to their clients' confidentiality. Faced with such difficult and time-consuming bureaucratic roadblocks, many patients simply choose not to fight for the treatment they need.

In addition, the methodology of many of the studies that report the efficacy of antidepressants is dubious. Most studies of these medications are commissioned by the drug companies themselves. The drug manufacturers typically don't submit studies with unfavorable results for publication in medical journals. In 2008, the *New England Journal of Medicine* published an article that uncovered this bias. The Freedom of Information Act was used to obtain access to all of the 74 FDA-registered studies (published and unpublished) on 12 antidepressants, from 1987 through 2004. In 94 percent of the *published* studies, antidepressants were shown to be effective. But in only 51 percent of *all* studies were antidepressants shown to be effective. By opting not to publish negative results, drug companies conceal from doctors and their patients that in half of all outcome studies, antidepressants are no better than placebos in relieving depression. Another analysis of 47 drug company studies on Prozac, Paxil, Zoloft, Effexor, Celexa, and Serzone published in *Prevention and Treatment* in 2002 showed that these drugs failed to outperform a placebo in the majority of trials.

Because antidepressants often fail to outperform placebos, the drug companies stack the deck in an attempt to demonstrate the efficacy of a new medication. Many new drug studies include a 2-week placebo "washout period" during which *all* prospective study subjects receive a placebo. Those subjects whose depression is relieved during the 2-week trial with the placebo are eliminated from the study. In doing so, drug manufacturers increase the probability that the remaining subjects will benefit more from the drug than from a placebo. This practice helps pharmaceutical companies get approval for new products.

The latest generation of antidepressant commercials addresses the fact that many patients are not fully helped by medication. They go something like this: "Many people who take antidepressants continue to experience some symptoms of depression. If you are taking an antidepressant and still suffering from symptoms of depression, consider *adding* Drug X. Ask your doctor if Drug X is right for you."

It's important to note that some people do benefit tremendously from antidepressants. I have worked with people whose lives were saved by antidepressants and many others whose lives were changed immeasurably for the better. Antidepressant treatment is especially useful for some severely depressed patients who would otherwise be unable to function. For them, medication provides the boost in energy and cognitive function they need to be able to engage in therapy and rise up out of their debilitating state.

But these drugs are not a panacea, and they frequently fail to deliver complete relief from depression. A meta-analysis of six studies including 718 patients published in 2010 in the *Journal of the American Medical Association* found that antidepressants were effective only for the most severely depressed patients. For patients with mild to moderate depression, and even some patients in the less-severe portion of the major depression category, antidepressants performed no better than a placebo.

Many people currently being treated with antidepressants do not fall into the severely depressed category of those who benefit most from taking these drugs. Antidepressants are now being prescribed to medicate symptoms of unhappiness and distress, which are not necessarily symptoms of a medical illness. By treating such symptoms only with chemicals, people are deprived of the opportunity to make the changes needed for a full and lasting recovery.

If you are experiencing feelings of depression, I recommend first utilizing natural approaches that address nutrition, exercise, sleep, exposure to bright light, and breathing to balance and energize your body. At the same time, psychotherapy and self-help strategies can help you to understand your thoughts and feelings and take active steps toward living a vital, meaningful life. If symptoms are severe, prolonged, and unresponsive to these approaches, medication should be considered.

The Mind-Body Mood Solution is designed to help you get to the root of your depressed feelings and make use of integrated, holistic methods to enhance your mood and your life. It can be used as a first step before resorting to medication, or in conjunction with medication. Each component of the program has been found to be helpful in boosting mood. I encourage you to explore all the strategies in the pages that follow and decide for yourself what works best for you.

Getting the Most out of the Program

I designed *The Mind-Body Mood Solution* to be comprehensive. Because you will have the opportunity to address several approaches at once, you will be able to progress more rapidly than if you made only one change. Your recovery will also be more durable. However, you might feel daunted by the prospect of working on more than one aspect of your life at a time. Please be reassured that you do not need to take on more than you feel you can do right now. And remember, each component of the program, when implemented by itself, has been shown to relieve depression. The synergy of the components in combination is especially powerful, but you don't have to engage in them all at once to reap benefit.

Each person is unique and different, as is each person's experience of depression. One person may be very tense, anxious, and agitated, with difficulty concentrating or sitting still. Another might be profoundly lethargic with little anxiety. Some people experience loss of appetite and difficulty sleeping, while others have a voracious appetite and sleep excessively. Some suffer muscular aches and pains, while others are pain free.

Clinical depression is severe depression, also called major depression. Patients with clinical depression have more symptoms and more severe symptoms than those with mild or moderate depression. A person with severe clinical depression may spend all day in bed, not getting up to bathe, dress, or engage in tasks of daily living. A more mildly depressed person may be functioning as a high-achieving executive, craftsperson, or busy parent of small children. What all depressed people share is a depressed mood and the feeling that life is not as enjoyable as it could be. People suffering from clinical depression may benefit from this book when used in combination with therapy and, possibly, medication. But the main audience for the book is people with mild to moderate depression.

Readiness Is Everything:
Determine Where to Focus Your Effort

To help you streamline your efforts and receive the maximum benefit from this program, I suggest that you complete the Readiness Assessment test on the following pages. Your results will give you an indication of what parts of the program are likely to yield the greatest benefit for you right now. All areas of the program are potentially valuable, but some may be more valuable for you at this time. Your results will help you customize the program to your specific needs. You will answer questions about how you think and feel and about your lifestyle. You will also be asked questions about your willingness to make changes in specific areas of your life.

This evaluation will identify the areas in which you are already strong, as well as those that could benefit from some additional attention. It will also pinpoint those areas you feel most ready to focus on now.

Readiness Assessment

Use the following scale to indicate your level of agreement with the statements in each section.

1 = strongly disagree
2 = disagree
3 = slightly disagree
4 = neutral

5 = slightly agree
6 = agree
7 = strongly agree

Nutrition

Statement	1	2	3	4	5	6	7
I almost always eat a healthy, well-balanced breakfast, lunch, and dinner.	1	2	3	4	5	6	7
I usually eat a healthy midmorning and midafternoon snack.	1	2	3	4	5	6	7
I do not skip meals.	1	2	3	4	5	6	7
I very rarely overeat.	1	2	3	4	5	6	7
My meals generally consist of whole foods such as fresh fruits, vegetables, lean proteins, and whole grains.	1	2	3	4	5	6	7
I rarely eat sweets, baked goods, fried foods, or breads.	1	2	3	4	5	6	7
I rarely eat highly processed sugary or starchy foods.	1	2	3	4	5	6	7
I take specific mood-enhancing vitamin and mineral supplements.	1	2	3	4	5	6	7
I am interested in learning about nutritional supplements I can take to improve my mood.	1	2	3	4	5	6	7
I look forward to making dietary changes that may help improve my mood.	1	2	3	4	5	6	7

Exercise

Statement	1	2	3	4	5	6	7
I exercise aerobically for at least 30 minutes a minimum of three times per week.	1	2	3	4	5	6	7
I exercise aerobically for at least 30 minutes a minimum of five times per week.	1	2	3	4	5	6	7

I achieve my target heart rate when exercising.	1 2 3 4 5 6 7
I do at least 20 minutes of strength-training exercise a minimum of two times per week.	1 2 3 4 5 6 7
I engage in physical activity (walking, outdoor work, housework) other than formal exercise for at least 30 minutes most days of the week.	1 2 3 4 5 6 7
I enjoy the time I spend exercising.	1 2 3 4 5 6 7
Exercise consistently improves my mood.	1 2 3 4 5 6 7
I don't let anything interfere with maintaining my exercise routine.	1 2 3 4 5 6 7
I am interested in learning ways to get more benefits from exercise.	1 2 3 4 5 6 7
I am willing to increase the time I devote to exercise in order to enhance my mood and my health.	1 2 3 4 5 6 7

Sleep

Getting a full night's sleep is not a problem for me.	1 2 3 4 5 6 7
I wake up in the morning feeling refreshed and energized for my day.	1 2 3 4 5 6 7
I never take prescription sleep medication or over-the-counter sleep aids to get to sleep.	1 2 3 4 5 6 7
I hardly ever have trouble getting back to sleep if I wake up in the middle of the night.	1 2 3 4 5 6 7
I am rarely sleepy during the day.	1 2 3 4 5 6 7
I rarely go on the computer or deal with work-related tasks late at night.	1 2 3 4 5 6 7
I have a relaxing evening routine that I engage in almost every evening.	1 2 3 4 5 6 7
I go to bed early enough to spend at least 7 to 8 hours in bed.	1 2 3 4 5 6 7
I am interested in learning new ways to relax so my sleep can become more restorative.	1 2 3 4 5 6 7
I am willing to change some habits in order to improve my sleep.	1 2 3 4 5 6 7

Light

In the winter I usually spend more than 30 minutes a day outdoors.	1 2 3 4 5 6 7
In the spring I usually spend more than 30 minutes a day outdoors.	1 2 3 4 5 6 7
In the summer I usually spend more than 30 minutes a day outdoors.	1 2 3 4 5 6 7
In the fall I usually spend more than 30 minutes a day outdoors.	1 2 3 4 5 6 7
I notice that I feel better on sunny days.	1 2 3 4 5 6 7
My mood tends to be better in warmer, sunnier months than in colder, darker months.	1 2 3 4 5 6 7
During the winter, I tend to feel more tired and depressed.	1 2 3 4 5 6 7
I tend to gain weight during the winter.	1 2 3 4 5 6 7
I know that bright light enhances my mood.	1 2 3 4 5 6 7
I use a high-intensity light box to enhance my mood.	1 2 3 4 5 6 7
I am interested in learning how exposure to bright light can enhance my mood and energy.	1 2 3 4 5 6 7
I am interested in learning how exposure to bright light can enhance my sleep.	1 2 3 4 5 6 7

Breathing

Please note that the first seven items in this section are scored differently than all the other items. That is, higher scores on the first seven items in this section indicate breathing difficulties.

From time to time, I feel breathless.	1 2 3 4 5 6 7
I am aware of holding my breath or sighing often.	1 2 3 4 5 6 7
My breathing is short and shallow.	1 2 3 4 5 6 7
I notice a tight feeling in my chest when I breathe.	1 2 3 4 5 6 7
I often have pain in my neck and shoulders.	1 2 3 4 5 6 7

I tend to hyperventilate.	1 2 3 4 5 6 7
I often feel like I am not getting enough air when I breathe.	1 2 3 4 5 6 7

Resume normal scoring.

I consciously engage in full, vigorous breathing to refresh and energize myself.	1 2 3 4 5 6 7
I consciously engage in slow, rhythmic breathing to relax and replenish myself.	1 2 3 4 5 6 7
I usually breathe slowly, naturally, and comfortably.	1 2 3 4 5 6 7
I am willing to invest some time and effort into learning healthy breathing practices.	1 2 3 4 5 6 7
I am interested in learning how to use my breath for relaxation and improving my mood.	1 2 3 4 5 6 7

Presence

I am able to experience what is happening in the present without being preoccupied by distracting thoughts.	1 2 3 4 5 6 7
I rarely ruminate about the past.	1 2 3 4 5 6 7
I don't worry very much about things that might happen in the future.	1 2 3 4 5 6 7
I see that my thoughts color my reality.	1 2 3 4 5 6 7
There is a part of me that is aware of my thoughts and emotions without being consumed by them.	1 2 3 4 5 6 7
When I have a feeling, I often take a moment to reflect on it before automatically reacting to it.	1 2 3 4 5 6 7
I maintain a regular meditation practice.	1 2 3 4 5 6 7
I am interested in learning how to become more fully present in the moment.	1 2 3 4 5 6 7
I am willing to devote some time each day to the practice of mindfulness or meditation.	1 2 3 4 5 6 7

Avoidance

I usually avoid confronting a difficult situation even if something positive could come out of it.	1 2 3 4 5 6 7						
I don't let disappointments keep me from getting involved with other people.	1 2 3 4 5 6 7						
I do not find myself dwelling on past disappointments.	1 2 3 4 5 6 7						
I don't procrastinate much.	1 2 3 4 5 6 7						
I don't have trouble moving forward in spite of disappointments.	1 2 3 4 5 6 7						
I am willing to let myself feel strong negative emotions.	1 2 3 4 5 6 7						
I am willing to take a look at how I have been avoiding my feelings.	1 2 3 4 5 6 7						
I am willing to feel, rather than avoid, my feelings.	1 2 3 4 5 6 7						

Judgment

I do not tend to see myself as inadequate.	1 2 3 4 5 6 7						
I recognize when I am being judgmental and try to be more accepting instead.	1 2 3 4 5 6 7						
I am not very self-critical.	1 2 3 4 5 6 7						
When I make an error or don't meet my own expectations, I can be compassionate toward myself for "falling short."	1 2 3 4 5 6 7						
I tend to be accepting of the mistakes and foibles of others.	1 2 3 4 5 6 7						
I am interested in becoming less self-critical and judgmental.	1 2 3 4 5 6 7						
I am willing to examine the way being judgmental impacts my relationships with others.	1 2 3 4 5 6 7						

Forgiveness and Gratitude

If someone hurts me, I don't hold a grudge against that person.	1 2 3 4 5 6 7
If someone hurts me, I tend to forgive that person.	1 2 3 4 5 6 7
I believe that forgiveness does not mean pardoning, excusing, or condoning wrongful acts.	1 2 3 4 5 6 7
If someone hurts me, I don't avoid that person.	1 2 3 4 5 6 7
If someone hurts me, I don't try to get even.	1 2 3 4 5 6 7
I feel grateful every day for the blessings in my life.	1 2 3 4 5 6 7
I make it a point to express gratitude to anyone in my life who is helpful to me.	1 2 3 4 5 6 7
When I focus on the blessings in my life, my mood lifts.	1 2 3 4 5 6 7
I make a point of focusing more on the things that went right than on the things that didn't.	1 2 3 4 5 6 7
I am willing to devote time to learning how to become more forgiving.	1 2 3 4 5 6 7
I am open to exploring more ways to experience gratitude in my life.	1 2 3 4 5 6 7

Action

I am involved in enjoyable activities.	1 2 3 4 5 6 7
I enjoy spending time doing things and making things with my hands.	1 2 3 4 5 6 7
I get together with friends often.	1 2 3 4 5 6 7
I make a point of doing things to help other people whenever I can.	1 2 3 4 5 6 7
If I'm feeling down, I make a point of getting out and doing something to lift my spirits.	1 2 3 4 5 6 7
I am ready to look at ways to increase my involvement in activities outside my home.	1 2 3 4 5 6 7
I am willing to reach out to friends and family and spend time with them.	1 2 3 4 5 6 7

Change

	1 2 3 4 5 6 7
I react well in a crisis.	1 2 3 4 5 6 7
I actively confront circumstances that interfere with my well-being.	1 2 3 4 5 6 7
I actively focus on ways to make my life better.	1 2 3 4 5 6 7
If I have a problem, I trust my intuition to help me find a way to deal with it.	1 2 3 4 5 6 7
Even in very difficult situations, I find the courage to take constructive action.	1 2 3 4 5 6 7
I reach out to others for help when I am facing a difficult problem.	1 2 3 4 5 6 7
I believe I can cope with any situation that I face.	1 2 3 4 5 6 7
I have a strong spiritual connection.	1 2 3 4 5 6 7
I am interested in learning ways to find strength and wisdom to confront difficult situations in my life.	1 2 3 4 5 6 7
I am willing to confront the changes I need to make in order to feel better.	1 2 3 4 5 6 7

Take a look at your scores. The areas in which you had the highest scores reflect your strengths. Continue to do what you are doing in those areas and feel good about the abilities and habits you already have. For instance, if you are already exercising aerobically five times a week for 30 minutes, continue to exercise and know that it will contribute to your optimal health and mood. You don't need to do more aerobic exercise now. Working out 7 days a week is not likely to boost your mood significantly more than your current 5 days a week. However, a subtle change in your routine, such as walking, biking, or jogging outdoors rather than indoors, might provide the sunlight you need to help boost your mood. Or exercising with a friend or taking a group class might provide mood-enhancing social contact. In areas where you have many high scores, plan on reading the relevant chapters and making only minor modifications to your current routine. In areas where your score is low, there is significant room for improvement and consequent enhancement of your mood.

The last two items in each section ask about your willingness to invest energy in making changes. If you have much room for improvement in an area and you are very willing to commit yourself to making changes, it will be worth devoting a good deal of your time and attention to the chapters that address those problems. If you have lots of room for improvement but little motivation to make changes in an area, read the chapter with the understanding that it may be helpful to you at a later time when you feel ready to tackle it.

Assess Your Level of Depression

It can be helpful to have an objective assessment of how depressed you are now. It will also be helpful to revisit and retake this assessment every 2 weeks to monitor your progress. By reviewing the results of your assessments and comparing them with your current results, you will be able to track several different symptoms of depression.

The assessment you will be completing is called the CES-D. It was developed by the Center for Epidemiologic Studies at the NIMH as a screening instrument for depression. As you respond to the questions below, you may become more aware of how you view yourself and various aspects of your life.

Center for Epidemiologic Studies Depression Scale

Circle the corresponding number of each statement that best describes how often you felt or behaved this way during the past week.

	RARELY OR NONE OF THE TIME (LESS THAN 1 DAY)	SOME OR A LITTLE OF THE TIME (1-2 DAYS)	OCCASIONALLY OR A MODERATE AMOUNT OF THE TIME (3-4 DAYS)	MOST OR ALL OF THE TIME (5-7 DAYS)
During the past week:				
1) I was bothered by things that usually don't bother me.	0	1	2	3
2) I did not feel like eating; my appetite was poor.	0	1	2	3
3) I felt that I could not shake off the blues even with help from my family and friends.	0	1	2	3
4) I felt that I was just as good as other people.	3	2	1	0
5) I had trouble keeping my mind on what I was doing.	0	1	2	3
6) I felt depressed.	0	1	2	3
7) I felt that everything I did was an effort.	0	1	2	3
8) I felt hopeful about the future.	3	2	1	0
9) I thought my life had been a failure.	0	1	2	3
10) I felt fearful.	0	1	2	3
11) My sleep was restless.	0	1	2	3
12) I was happy.	3	2	1	0
13) I talked less than usual.	0	1	2	3

	RARELY OR NONE OF THE TIME (LESS THAN 1 DAY)	SOME OR A LITTLE OF THE TIME (1–2 DAYS)	OCCASIONALLY OR A MODERATE AMOUNT OF THE TIME (3–4 DAYS)	MOST OR ALL OF THE TIME (5–7 DAYS)
14) I felt lonely.	0	1	2	3
15) People were unfriendly.	0	1	2	3
16) I enjoyed life.	3	2	1	0
17) I had crying spells.	0	1	2	3
18) I felt sad.	0	1	2	3
19) I felt that people disliked me.	0	1	2	3
20) I could not get "going".	0	1	2	3

The scoring system for the CES-D:

If you scored between 10 and 15, *you may be mildly depressed.*

If you scored between 16 and 25, *you may be moderately depressed.*

If you scored above 25, *you may be significantly depressed.*

Your score on the CES-D will give you an overall assessment of your current level of depression. Keep in mind that this is just one way of assessing how you are feeling. If we looked more closely at other aspects of depression, such as energy level or activity level, your depression score might be substantially different. Also be aware that your score provides a snapshot of how you are doing right now, and it is likely to change as you progress through the program. As you retake the assessment every other week, your responses may provide new clues as to which areas you most want to focus on.

If you are significantly depressed, you may benefit from the one-to-one support and guidance that a psychotherapist provides.

Some people are better able to use the elements of the program if they are working with a therapist. If you are less severely depressed, working with a therapist may still be very helpful. Even if you are capable of using the approaches in this book on your own, feedback from a professional may be extremely valuable. You will find information about how to select a therapist in Chapter 14.

Find Support

As you use this program, it will be helpful for you to have someone to turn to for support. This person should be someone you trust, such as a caring friend, family member, clergy person, or mentor. Let this person know that you are experiencing depression and explain that you are using the strategies in this book to help you get better. Ask if he or she would be willing to support you in this effort. If the answer is yes, it might be a good idea for him or her to read this book, too. It will be helpful to discuss your progress with your support person at least once a week.

Another wonderful way to find support and contact is by joining a support group. If you or a loved one is dealing with an addiction, you may find support through a 12-step program. There are also support groups for those who are facing a medical illness or are recently bereaved. A small class can also be a good way to connect with others who are pursuing a similar interest. For instance, you might enroll in a yoga class, a meditation class, art classes, or exercise classes. Other ways to connect with people in a group context include religious groups, volunteer groups, and book discussion groups. If you enjoy sports or outdoor activities, then you might want to join a group in which you can participate in such activities, such as a bowling team, a tennis league, a running group, a hiking club, or a basketball team.

What If You're Already Too Busy?

If you already feel overextended, you will need to shift some priorities in order to find time to engage in the program. You may need to opt out of some nonessential commitments. Keep in mind that if you devote time to caring for yourself now, you will be better able to care for others in the future. If you have children, you will be a much better parent to them if you are healthy and positive. You will be a better spouse, friend, family member, or employee if you are feeling and functioning at your best. You are worth taking care of, and that requires an investment of your time.

Take Time to Reflect on Your Experience

At the end of each chapter, you will find several questions that provide opportunities for reflection. Take some time to think about each of these questions and write your responses in the space provided.

You will also find a Daily Check-In form on page 242. Using it to record your activities, feelings, and realizations will help you monitor your progress from day to day. When you go back to review your answers after a number of days or weeks, you will be able to spot patterns and get a sense of which tools are helping you most. Feel free to fill in only the sections of the Check-In on which you are focusing.

Get a Physical

Many symptoms of depression can be caused by specific medical conditions. Before starting the program, it is important to see your doctor for a medical evaluation to make sure you are not suffering from one of these conditions. Some of the more common medical causes of depression are hypothyroidism, diabetes, lupus, and some types of cancer. Any of the diseases on the following list may cause depression in some people:

- AIDS
- Adrenal overactivity (Cushing's disease)
- Adrenal underactivity (Addison's disease)
- Autoimmune conditions, including lupus erythematosus and rheumatoid arthritis

- Cancer
- Cerebrovascular disease
- Chronic fatigue immune deficiency syndrome (CFIDS)
- Chronic pain
- Diabetes
- Head trauma
- Heart disease
- Infections
- Lyme disease
- Lung disease
- Multiple sclerosis
- Parkinson's disease
- Thyroid disease

Please don't allow this list to add to your worries. It's unlikely that your depression is stemming from one of these conditions. Nevertheless, it is important to rule out the possibility of medical conditions before embarking on a mood-enhancement program.

PART I

WORKING WITH YOUR BODY

Chapter 1

EATING FOR WELLNESS

Let food be your medicine and medicine be your food.

HIPPOCRATES, 500 BC

The food you eat has a profound effect on your energy, emotions, motivation, and outlook on life. The typical American diet, which is high in refined sugar and processed carbohydrates, causes a spike in blood sugar followed by a rapid crash, which can leave you feeling fatigued, hungry, irritable, depressed, or mentally confused. This vital connection between food and mood means that many cases of depression improve rapidly when changes are made to a patient's diet, including nutritional supplementation.

As we begin this chapter, I want to give you a heads up. At certain points, I'll be presenting scientific information about the connection between nutrition and mood. If you find it helpful, read on. But if all of this information feels a little overwhelming right now, feel free to skim or skip the sections you're struggling with and come back to them later.

Eating food that contains high levels of allergens, trans fats, and toxic substances such as herbicides, pesticides, and antibiotics can cause chronic inflammation in the body. Inflammation is a result of the immune system's effort to neutralize organisms and substances that it perceives as a threat. Although the immune system's response is intended to protect you from harm, it drains your energy, leaving you feeling sluggish, fatigued, and unmotivated. Think of the last time you had the flu: All of your body's resources were directed toward fighting the infection, and you had little energy left over to feel focused, energetic, or upbeat. The only difference between fighting an infection caused by illness and mounting an inflammatory response to a dietary trigger is that your body generally kills off an offending microbe and you feel better—whereas inflammation caused by poor diet continues until you change your diet.

What does this mean if you suffer from depression? It can be difficult to differentiate between the symptoms of a mood disorder and the malaise caused by poor or inadequate nutrition. If you experience a lack of focus, negative thinking, and an inability to greet the day with enthusiasm, you may describe yourself as depressed. But your symptoms may actually be related to your diet.

One way to determine whether your diet is affecting your mood is to examine your eating patterns. Are you eating healthy foods? Are you using food as a comfort to assuage the disappointments and tensions in your life? Are you skipping meals or eating too much in one meal, causing your blood sugar to soar and then drop like a roller coaster?

For some people who suffer from depressed mood and negative outlook, improving diet, adding specific vitamin and mineral supplements, and changing eating patterns can make a remarkable difference. In many cases these changes reverse the symptoms of depression without therapy or antidepressant medication. It is therefore important to determine to what extent dietary considerations are influencing your mood.

Bill's Story

Bill typically began his day by eating what he believed to be a reasonably healthy breakfast, consisting of a blueberry muffin with a cup of coffee and orange juice. On some days, for a midmorning snack, he would eat a doughnut or a bagel with cream cheese, both of which were usually available to him at work.

When he remembered to eat lunch, he often ordered either a turkey sandwich on a roll with potato chips and a soft drink or a cheeseburger. If he felt especially hungry, he would add french fries. On other days, he would skip both the snack and the lunch entirely.

By about 3:00 in the afternoon, Bill would feel lethargic and generally eat an "energy bar" from the vending machine with a cup of coffee or a caffeinated soft drink. After his midafternoon snack, he felt more focused. But by dinner he felt exhausted again and always ate more than a single portion. His evening meal usually consisted of a large serving of meat, a couple of rolls with margarine, a small serving of vegetables, and a large bowl of ice cream for dessert. Other times he ate a double serving of pasta with meat sauce, or even an entire pizza. Very often he ate an evening snack, such as chips or popcorn.

Bill was also depressed. He felt he was in a dead-end job but had too little energy and motivation to seek a different career path. He often felt passed over for advancement by his supervisor. Bill's symptoms included irritability, fatigue, lethargy, weight gain, and apathy.

If Bill's food choices represent a typical day for you, changing your diet might significantly improve your mood. The food choices Bill made not only lacked healthy vitamins and minerals; they were also high in fat, calories, sodium, refined carbohydrates, and sugar. His bad habit of skipping lunch caused his blood sugar to plummet, leaving him ravenous by afternoon. The energy bar he then ate contained little protein compared with its extremely high carbohydrate and sugar content. Eating this snack raised his blood sugar level dramatically, which dropped just in time for dinner, again resulting in excessive hunger, poor food choices, and overeating.

When Bill came to see me, the first thing I suggested was that we adjust his diet. He began to eat a healthy breakfast every day: either fresh fruit and a whole grain English muffin or an egg-white omelet with whole grain toast spread with almond butter, and coffee. He regularly planned for his midmorning snack, which consisted of whole grain crackers or veggie sticks with hummus or natural peanut butter.

He brought organic soups, salads, and sandwich wraps filled with lean protein and veggies to work for lunch. He would eat half of the wrap at lunch and save the rest for his afternoon snack, which also included a piece of fruit such as an apple, orange, or banana. And because he wasn't starving at dinnertime, he was able to make sensible choices then, too. He started eating more fish and other lean proteins, accompanied by lots of veggies.

Within days, Bill began to notice a difference in his mood. He discovered that eating healthier foods and regular meals and snacks not only improved his focus and attention but also helped him lose weight and feel more confident. Why? Bill's diet now supplied him with the amino acids that his body needed to make and regulate serotonin and dopamine. These two neurotransmitters—chemicals that relay signals across different parts of our brains—have a dramatic impact on mood. Seventy percent of our serotonin is found in the intestinal tract, and the food we eat plays a major role in its production. As he began to feel more positive about his skills in the workplace, Bill's colleagues noticed his buoyant attitude, and eventually his supervisor recommended him for a different position within the company, which entailed a salary increase.

The best strategy for maintaining balanced blood sugar levels is to avoid eating high-carbohydrate foods that contain refined flour and sugar. Eating some protein at every meal slows the absorption of healthy carbohydrates into the bloodstream. To keep your body and mood in balance, it's also important to eat three balanced meals and two healthy snacks every day. Eat one snack at midmorning, when you hit your energy slump (about 3 hours after breakfast), and the other as a healthy midafternoon snack (about 3 to 4 hours after lunch). Don't skip meals.

The quality of the food you eat is just as important as the quantity. I recommend purchasing organic produce, whole grains, and grass-fed (or "free-range") animal protein such as beef, chicken, turkey, and eggs. Animals that are not treated with antibiotics, hormones, and growth stimulants do not produce meat that causes inflammation.

One of the best ways to change your eating habits is to use mindful eating techniques. You can practice mindfulness by slowing down as you eat, focusing on one bite at a time. Reading or working at the computer while you mindlessly eat can distract you from the pleasures of delicious, healthy food.

Mindful eating can be especially helpful if you tend to overeat or make unhealthy food choices. By savoring each bite of your sandwich or focusing on the sweetness of the melon or strawberry on your tongue, you will experience heightened satisfaction in eating a small, appropriate serving of food. Eating healthy food feels good, and you can amplify that good feeling with mindful eating.

Try this experiment. Eat a small piece of cantaloupe or apple very slowly. Taste it fully. It's hard to overeat fruit, because it's high in fiber and natural sugars. Eat another piece of fruit; delightful again—right?

Now eat a small piece of chocolate. Savor its sweetness. Let it melt in your mouth. Now swallow. Try another small piece of chocolate. Is it as sweet as the first? Very likely it is not. Most chocolate is high in refined white sugar and hits all the sweetness receptors on your tongue in the first bite. The receptors are now blocked, and the sweetness of your next bite of chocolate doesn't register. It doesn't taste sweet; in fact, it may have no taste whatsoever. No comfort, no chocolate "joy." No wonder we mindlessly keep eating more, chasing the sweet "hit" we got from the first piece.

Mindful eating helps us slow down and enjoy our food and increases our awareness that we are nurturing ourselves with the building blocks of life. When we make the right food choices and eat mindfully, our bodies can build the biochemicals that relieve stress and provide us with a sense of peace, joy, and relaxation.

Due to many factors, however, dietary choices alone may not supply enough of the minerals and raw materials needed to alleviate depression. The nutrients provided by specific foods we eat are needed to support healthy brain chemistry. At night, during the deepest stage of sleep, our bodies convert nutrients from the food we ate during the day into a powerful reserve of natural antianxiety and antidepressant neurotransmitters. Some of these neurotransmitters, such as dopamine and norepinephrine, stimulate feelings of enthusiasm and excitement; others, such as serotonin and gamma-aminobutyric acid (GABA), help us feel calm and tranquil. If we don't get the necessary nutrients from our diet, our bodies are less able to combat depressed moods.

It's not just about eating the right foods, however—our bodies also have to metabolize food properly to gain nutritive benefit. Some people may not have enough of the healthy intestinal bacteria that line the digestive tract and aid in the absorption of the nutrients from food. Often, people who lack sufficient healthy bacteria have recently taken a course of antibiotics, which wipe out even the good bacteria. The active cultures in yogurt and probiotic foods and supplements containing acidophilus and bifidus bacteria can help to repopulate the gut with the healthy bacteria that aid digestion.

Excessive stress can also cause our bodies to use up our biochemical reserves too quickly. For instance, prolonged stress can cause depletion of B vitamins and calcium. In such cases, vitamin and mineral supplementation may be necessary for you to function at your best.

Serotonin is the primary antianxiety and antidepressant biochemical. When your body produces enough serotonin, you will have the requisite brain chemistry to support a positive, confident outlook and a flexible, easygoing manner. When you are deficient in serotonin, you may experience irritability, anxiety, negative thinking, and difficulty sleeping.

In order to create serotonin, your body needs a precursor chemical: an amino acid called tryptophan. Tryptophan is found in high-protein foods such as turkey, beef, eggs, and some dairy products, including cheese. Though these foods have been available to us for centuries and are widely consumed, the antibiotics, pesticides, and other toxic chemicals that have been added to our food supply in recent years have altered the nutritive benefit of the foods we eat. Whereas animals once ate a diet of grass and plants, which provided them with nutrients (including tryptophan) that were passed on to us when we ate their meat, most livestock today is fed grain, soy, growth hormones, and antibiotics. Thus, it's harder for us to get the nutrients our brains (and the rest of our bodies) need in order to function properly.

Some foods and food additives can contribute to depression. Processed sugar and high-fructose corn syrup can cause an immediate spike in blood sugar that is energizing in a way that makes some people feel hyperactive. However, prolonged, excessive consumption ultimately results in blood sugar lows that fuel exhaustion and depression. Many depressed people improve dramatically when they eliminate sugar from their diets. In addition, stimulants such as caffeine, diet pills, or aspartame (NutraSweet) directly interfere with the relaxing effects of serotonin.

When the brain does not receive the nutrients it needs to properly regulate our neurotransmitters, we may experience prolonged periods of stress or suffer from chronic pain. This pain is often caused by inflammation and lack of endorphins, our body's "feel-good" chemicals that promote feelings of well-being and help alleviate physical pain. Stress and chronic pain also contribute to the depletion of our serotonin reserves. One way to help counter the effects of the modern American diet is to supplement it with amino acid combinations of 5-hydroxytryptophan (5-HTP), tryptophan itself, or an herb called St. John's wort, which helps increase serotonin levels naturally.

Another set of biochemicals involved in maintaining a healthy mood are called catecholamines. These substances, which include dopamine, norepinephrine, and adrenaline, help us feel alert, upbeat, and energized. When we are deficient in one or more of these biochemicals, we may feel emotionally flat, lethargic, and unfocused.

Tyrosine is an amino acid needed to produce catecholamines. It is present in high-protein foods such as beef, fish, eggs, peanuts, almonds, avocados, and hummus. Tyrosine deficiency can be caused by a low-protein diet, prolonged sleep deprivation, or excessive stress. Many people with low catecholamine levels try to compensate for their lack of energy with stimulants such as caffeine, But while drinking a caffeinated beverage may temporarily increase energy and alertness, it does not provide the raw materials the body needs in order to sustain adequate levels of catecholamines.

Tyrosine is also needed to make thyroid hormones, which regulate our metabolism. Too little tyrosine in our bodies literally depletes us of life-force energy. No wonder people low in thyroid hormones often feel wiped out and overwhelmed. For people unable to make adequate supplies of catecholamines from dietary sources, adding the supplement L-tyrosine can dramatically enhance mood, energy, and the ability to focus.

Our bodies produce other biochemicals that help us feel relaxed, calm, and stress free. GABA, an amino acid, is our own natural antianxiety biochemical. The widely prescribed tranquilizer known as Valium is a synthetic form of this biochemical. GABA turns off the overstimulating effects of stress and reduces adrenaline levels. When we don't have adequate levels of GABA, we feel keyed up, stressed, and burdened by the demands of life. If you are feeling overwhelmed by the tasks of daily living, supplementation with GABA may help you feel calmer and better able to manage stress.

Our bodies also produce endorphins, which are biochemicals that help us feel comfort, pleasure, delight, and joy. Endorphins are our own natural pain medicine and are produced in response to experiences of physical pain, grief, or loss. When our bodies are depleted of endorphins, our losses feel unmanageable, and we may become overly sensitive and emotionally fragile. The amino acid phenylalanine (DLPA), the building block of endorphins, can be used to supplement dietary sources. Vitamins and minerals also boost endorphin levels. For example, B vitamins, magnesium, and omega-3 fatty acids all help promote the production of endorphins. Animal protein is a rich source of B vitamins, and dark chocolate, nuts, and spinach are excellent sources of magnesium. Both fish and fortified eggs are good sources of omega-3 fatty acids.

Taking a daily multivitamin that provides your required levels of these and other vitamins and minerals can help your brain produce the biochemicals needed for you to feel energetic, hopeful, focused, joyful, and calm. I recommend taking an omega-3 supplement in addition to your multivitamin. The combination of the two can broadly protect you from nutritional deficiencies that affect your mood and your overall health.

Vitamin D

One of the most overlooked contributors to depression, especially seasonal depression, is vitamin D deficiency. Among its many functions, vitamin D plays an important role in the healthy functioning of the nervous system. The epidemic of vitamin D deficiency is a product of our modern lifestyle—our bodies manufacture vitamin D through exposure to sunlight, and very few of us spend enough time outdoors to get sufficient vitamin D. People living in colder, northern climates almost always have low levels of this nutrient especially in the winter. The main dietary source of vitamin D is fatty fish, such as mackerel, salmon, or herring.

How much vitamin D do you actually need? I don't believe that the FDA's recommended daily allowance (RDA), which is 400 international units (IU) of vitamin D_3, is sufficient for optimal nervous system functioning. People who have a vitamin D deficiency may need between 2,000 and 10,000 IU of vitamin D_3 a day. To determine whether you have a vitamin D deficiency, ask your doctor for a blood test. The ideal blood level for vitamin D is 50 to 80 nanograms per milliliter. If you are one of the estimated 240 million Americans who are deficient in this vitamin, consider increasing your dietary intake of vitamin D, taking a vitamin D supplement, and spending a few more minutes a day outdoors. The more of your skin that is exposed to sunlight, without sunscreen, the more vitamin D your body will produce. Sunscreen blocks the absorption of UVB rays, which stimulate your skin to manufacture vitamin D. For most people, 15 minutes a day of early afternoon sun is sufficient, yet not enough to cause sunburn and raise skin cancer risk. If you live in a seasonal climate, you won't be able to get enough UVB rays in winter to produce vitamin D. During those months, you will need to rely on supplements to maintain an adequate vitamin D level. It can take up to 6 months for vitamin D supplementation to bring your level into the optimal range, so be patient and work with your doctor to determine your optimal dosage.

Dora, a 48-year-old nurse, was exhausted and despondent when she came into my office. Her sleep was severely disrupted by her work schedule. In addition, her spirit and energy had been drained for 2 years by a complicated malpractice case. It was as if a giant curtain had dropped and her soul was out of sight backstage. She spoke about her fear and anger about the lawsuit, but her emotions seemed muffled. I was worried about Dora. Her flat emotional state and low energy level made me concerned about her ability to meet the demands of her hospital job.

I suggested that she ask to be taken off the night shift, which was interfering with her ability to get restorative sleep. I recommended that she work with a therapist at home, and I gave her the names of several therapists in her area. She also began taking 5,000 IU of vitamin D a day. When I saw Dora again 5 months later, she looked like a different person. She radiated vitality. Her smile was broad and genuine. She shared with me that she had tried to find a therapist, but had not found one she felt comfortable with. She did manage to be relieved of working the night shift, and her sleep had improved immediately. She had begun taking vitamin D supplements as soon as she left Canyon Ranch. She gradually felt better, and pointed to her vitamin D treatment as the key to her recovery. She was feeling much more optimistic about the lawsuit, and she was dating a man she had met a few months earlier. I spoke with Dora again almost a year later. She was continuing to feel more energetic and upbeat, she had won the lawsuit, and she was in a relationship with the man she had met the year before.

B Vitamins

Another common nutritional deficiency that may contribute to feelings of depression is a low level of the B vitamins, including folate, B_6, and B_{12}. This deficiency impairs production of the neurotransmitters involved in maintaining a healthy mood and good cognitive functioning. These vitamins also play a role in helping the receptors on cells receive messages from neurotransmitters. When these nutrients are supplied to the body via diet or supplementation, people deficient in B vitamins may improve rapidly and dramatically, within a few days. Many depressed people who are vitamin B deficient improve on the following regimen of supplementation:

- Folate (also known as folic acid): 800 micrograms
- B_6 or pyridoxine: 50 milligrams
- B_{12}: 1,000 micrograms

You can also get vitamin B through the following dietary sources:

- Folate: Beef liver, leafy green vegetables, citrus fruits, dried beans and peas
- Vitamin B_6: Meat, dairy, eggs, tuna, potatoes, chickpeas, bananas, cauliflower
- Vitamin B_{12}: Meat, dairy, eggs

Absorption of vitamin B_{12} from dietary sources can be impaired due to digestive disorders (such as acid reflux) and the medications used to treat these conditions (such as acid blockers). Aging can also contribute to the body's impaired ability to absorb vitamin B_{12}. For some people, it may be necessary to bypass the digestive system with B_{12} shots or under-the-tongue tablets that are absorbed directly into the bloodstream. If you are over the age of 60 or have a history of acid reflux or other digestive disorders such as Crohn's disease, it is especially important to have your doctor test your levels of B vitamins and prescribe the appropriate dosage and form of supplements, if needed.

Before adding any supplements to your diet, consult with a physician, nutritionist, naturopath, or psychiatrist with nutritional training. Many conditions can be made worse by inadvertently choosing the wrong supplement or dosage. Review your diet, medical history, and mental health symptoms with your practitioner. He or she may recommend laboratory testing to determine the levels of specific vitamins, neurotransmitters, and neurohormones in your body. Be aware that these tests can be quite expensive and may not be covered by your health insurance. Your practitioner should be familiar with the costs and be willing to streamline the tests ordered to help minimize your out-of-pocket costs. In many cases, experienced practitioners can detect deficiencies and prescribe supplements based on your symptoms alone, without ordering such tests.

The chart below provides an overview of the biochemicals needed to support optimal brain function and cognitive health, and which foods or supplements can help supply them. For more detailed information, see the Complementary Supplement Chart on page 294.

Nutrition-Mood Chart

SYMPTOMS	BIOCHEMICALS NEEDED	FOOD SOURCES	SUPPLEMENTS
Irritability, worry, negative thinking, trouble sleeping	Serotonin	Turkey, grains, fruits	Tryptophan, 5-HTP, St. John's wort
Lack of energy, sluggishness, exhaustion, flat emotions, no motivation, lack of focus, depressed mood	Dopamine, epinephrine, adrenaline	Fish, beef, eggs, peanuts, almonds	L-tyrosine
Overwhelming thoughts, stress, anxiety, tension	GABA	High protein foods balanced with healthy carbohydrates (vegetables)	GABA, L-theanine
Chronic physical pain, grief, loss, and isolation; oversensitivity or vulnerability	Endorphins	Fish, eggs, chicken, cottage cheese	Omega-3 fatty acids, DLPA, B vitamins
Difficulty falling or staying asleep	Melatonin, serotonin, magnesium, GABA	Turkey, beef, eggs, dairy	Magnesium, melatonin, GABA, 5-hydroxytryptophan (5-HTP)

Even when symptoms of depression or anxiety are not exclusively related to diet, improving your nutritional intake can quickly restore enough energy and motivation to engage in a program of self-improvement. For example, the increased energy level experienced as a result of improved diet or supplementation may make it possible to engage in regular exercise or give you the energy needed to face important life issues that you may have previously felt too tired to address.

Jennifer's Story

When I first met Jennifer, she was frightened and tearful. A tall, thin, attractive woman in her late twenties, she had become depressed during the previous 6 months and was frightened that her marriage of 18 months was falling apart. She was having trouble sleeping and was finding it increasingly difficult to summon up the energy and motivation to make it out the door in the morning. When she did manage to get to the restaurant where she worked, she had trouble focusing on the customers. Her characteristically cheerful and outgoing personality had become subdued and withdrawn. She was preoccupied with anxiety about her marriage and her own fragile emotional state. She had been depressed in her early twenties and feared that she could be returning to that dark, despairing place.

The first step was to evaluate Jennifer for any medical or nutritional factors that could be contributing to her depression. Her thin stature and recent transition to a strict vegetarian diet made me wonder if she was getting adequate nutrition. I referred her to a medical colleague, who discovered nutritional deficiencies that could be impacting her mood. She was low in vitamin B_6 and several amino acids that are the building blocks of neurotransmitters that are essential for feelings of well-being. To remedy these deficiencies, Jennifer started taking a B_6 supplement in addition to the multivitamin she was already taking, and she added free-range animal protein to her previously vegetarian diet.

The evaluation also uncovered that she was very low in tryptophan, the building block of serotonin, which promotes calmness and well-being, and melatonin, which promotes sleep. To boost her serotonin and melatonin levels, she started taking 5-hydroxytryptophan, which provides the body with the raw material for producing serotonin and melatonin.

Jennifer's lab test results also showed evidence of undesirable bacteria and yeast in her intestines. Bad bacteria can "steal" tryptophan from the body and lower serotonin and melatonin levels. To remedy this, Jennifer cut back on sugar, dairy, and fermented foods such as alcohol and vinegar. All of these foods can feed the growth of unhealthy gut bacteria and yeast. She started taking oil of oregano to aid in eliminating the yeast and bad bacteria. In addition, she took probiotics, which support the growth of good bacteria in the intestines, and digestive enzymes to help her body absorb and utilize the food and supplements she was taking in. Some examples of probiotics are acidophilus and bifidus, both of which can be purchased in health food stores. Some foods such as yogurt also contain probiotic bacteria.

Within a week of making these changes to her diet, Jennifer felt much better and was tremendously encouraged. She was also more emotionally stable, energetic, and enthusiastic. With increased energy, she was able to resume an exercise regimen. She had been an avid exerciser in the past, but had stopped working out when she got married. She enjoyed running, yoga, and cycling. We set up a plan that included walking/running, cycling, yoga, and dancing. She purchased two yoga videos that she used at home every day. She also started going for long walks. Four weeks after our first meeting, Jennifer had joined a gym and was working out regularly. Her body was responding to her efforts with more energy and increased muscle tone.

Jennifer started to feel more productive and engaged at work and gained confidence in herself. She was able to focus constructively on her marriage and the friendships that she had neglected while she was depressed. During the next several weeks, Jennifer worked with me on resolving the issues in her marriage and moving forward. She also learned new ways of handling her thoughts and emotions that helped to channel her energy constructively.

Reflective Questions

In the spaces below, please write down the foods that you eat in a typical day. Even though your food choices may vary from day to day, try to give a picture of what types of foods you eat most often. Then take some time to reflect on how you could change your diet to improve your mood.

A sample of my daily food intake:

Breakfast:

_____

_____

_____

Lunch:

_____

_____

_____

Dinner:

_____

_____

_____

Snacks:

_____

_____

_____

1. I realize I do _____ do not _____ eat some foods that are unhealthy for me and may be affecting my mood.

2. Some food choices I could change to improve my eating habits and my mood are:

_____

_____

_____

3. When examining my snacking habits, I notice I do _____ do not _____ snack regularly in the midmorning or midafternoon, which may affect my blood sugar levels. Some ways I can improve the quality of my snacking are:

_____

_____

_____

4. I do _____ do not _____ take mineral and vitamin supplements. Additional vitamins/supplements I can ask my physician or complementary health practitioner about are:

_____

_____

_____

5. When I tried the fruit and chocolate experiment described on page 33, I noticed:

_____

_____

_____

6. I notice that I overeat _____ and/or eat certain foods _____ for comfort. Some of the comfort foods I have been eating that may be affecting my mood include:

_____

_____

_____

7. When I practice mindful eating, I notice:

_____

_____

_____

Chapter 2

THE IMPORTANCE OF EXERCISE

One of your most powerful sources of positive energy is physical activity. Exercise is a potent antidepressant and a natural antidote to the constriction and stagnation of depression. Your body is hardwired to move. The intricate connections among your muscles and bones, the flow of blood that carries oxygen and nutrients to those muscles, and the complex web of nerves originating in your spinal cord and brain all support your ability to walk, run, and lift heavy objects. Nature designed our bodies to move in ways that enabled our ancient ancestors to survive under harsh circumstances. As such, nature provided a reward-based incentive for engaging in strenuous physical activity: a flood of mood-boosting neurotransmitters.

If you doubt that we are hardwired to engage in and enjoy physical activity, stop by an elementary school as the bell rings for recess. You'll see a flood of children streaming onto the playground, enthusiastically jumping rope, throwing balls, and climbing on a jungle gym. If they are not yet hooked on iPods and cell phones, and if they are not told they have to "exercise," kids will naturally engage in physical activity for the sheer joy of it. They call it *play*.

If you were once one of those children, you may remember the feeling of liberation when you could get away from sitting at your school desk for an hour and run free outdoors. I hope that as you engage in physical activity now, you can experience some of the joy that comes from being free to move your body in a spirit of play. Perhaps you have experienced it at some time in your adult life while riding your bike, swimming in the ocean, dancing with abandon, or walking through the woods.

Physical activity is a powerful antidepressant, and it can be an important part of your overall program for enhancing your mood. However, if you are depressed and have been sedentary for a long time, I realize that the prospect of exercise may seem daunting, especially since depression can bring fatigue and a blockage of energy. The prospect of having to exercise may feel overwhelming, like one more obligation you have to fulfill. Sometimes I wish I could avoid using the word *exercise* because of all the negative connotations and unpleasant associations it evokes. In our culture it is something we often are told we *should* do, and thus it is usually not something we *want* to do.

Exercise is at least as effective in boosting your mood as many antidepressant medications. Over 500 studies have demonstrated that physical exercise can reduce anxiety, enhance mood, and manage stress. Most of this research has focused on the effects of aerobic exercise. Aerobic exercise elevates your heart and breathing rates. Activities such as walking, hiking, biking, jogging, swimming, and dancing are all examples of aerobic exercise. Participating in any of these activities can help to elevate your mood. A smaller but significant number of studies have shown that engaging in strength-training exercise, such as lifting weights, also has a positive impact on mood. Just 30 minutes of exercise three times a week is enough to substantially lift your mood.

Jerry's Story

Jerry was a guest at Canyon Ranch who came to see me about his feelings of depression. I'd heard about Jerry from colleagues, but nothing could have prepared me for the broken man who came through my door. Ruddy-faced and overweight with sparse, gray hair, he appeared much older than his 58 years. At 5'10" and 242 pounds, he was on medication to manage his high blood pressure of 156/104. Though he was revered as a luminary in his field, his bright light was considerably dimmed by the aura of tense exhaustion that surrounded him like a dark cloud.

"I'm supposed to be on a cruise with my wife this week. When I got home from my last consulting trip to Asia, I was fried. Eighteen-hour days, five countries in 2 weeks—I was too wired to sleep. I'd order room service and a bottle of wine. I'd pass out, wake up 3 hours later, and do it all over again. I got home exhausted and irritable. My wife and I have been fighting since the moment I got home. She canceled the cruise, called Canyon Ranch, and set this up for me. I have never been to a place like this, but I'm a captive audience for the next 7 days. They told me I should see you first. I have a bunch of other appointments booked, but I really don't have the foggiest idea of where to begin."

"Let's begin right here," I said. "You made a good choice to come here."

"I had no choice. This was my wife's idea."

"Then your wife made a good choice."

"Okay, now what?"

"What are you hoping to get out of your stay?"

"I told you this wasn't my idea."

"I know, Jerry. You weren't exactly looking for a trip to a holistic wellness center. But if you could gain something while you are here, what would you like that to be?"

"Okay . . . well, I want to be able to sleep for more than 3 hours a night. I want to wake up feeling relaxed and energetic, not dreading the day. I want my mind to stop racing all the time and my blood pressure to come down. I want to get off this treadmill of a life and look forward to waking up in the morning. I don't want to keep fighting with my wife, and I want her to be happy that I'm coming home. Is that enough?"

"That's a good start."

"It all sounds great, but there's a lot of pressure on me and serious problems to solve. The day after I get home, I'm back on the road for 2 weeks, eight clients in six cities in 14 days. I need the cash flow. I have to get my sanity back and fix this with my wife. I've been really nasty, and she's had it."

For a man who loved to be in control, Jerry's life was careening dangerously. A widely respected consultant, he traveled 500,000 miles a year giving high-paid advice to corporate CEOs and boards of directors. He was at the pinnacle of his industry, but in his personal life he felt he was near the bottom of an abyss. His body was out of control, and his marriage was slipping away.

I have worked with hundreds of extraordinarily successful men and women like Jerry who were at the top of their field. Whether they hailed from Wall Street, Madison Avenue, Hollywood, Broadway, or Capitol Hill, they were accustomed to being respected experts at work, yet they became slaves to a body in the midst of a painful rebellion, a spirit in despair, or personal relationships on the brink of ending. Obviously, career and financial success are no guarantee of personal health and happiness, but success does not necessarily require the sacrifice of health and happiness, either. Over the years, I've seen too many people who bought into the idea that career success necessarily comes at the expense of personal health, happiness, and relationships. In our overscheduled, competitive culture, too many people believe you have to do whatever it takes to be successful, even if it means sacrificing your health and your happiness.

Jerry glanced at his watch. "Uh-oh, time's up. What now?"

"Take a hike."

"Very funny, doc!"

"I'm not kidding." I had glanced at Jerry's schedule lying on the table in my office. "You're scheduled for the one o'clock hike up Mount Greylock. The best thing you could do right now is get outside, walk up into the mountains, and clear your head."

"I haven't been hiking in years, and I'm exhausted."

"Enjoy the hike . . . and Jerry, leave the BlackBerry in your room."

"I need to be reachable."

"Let's talk about that tomorrow." He furrowed his brow at me in mock frustration. "I mean it, Jerry. There's no reception up there." Jerry managed a wry laugh. I sensed a slight hint of relief as he picked up his bag and flashed a half smile on his way out of my office.

Jerry's habit of being "reachable" was keeping him disconnected from himself. Like so many hardworking high achievers, he had internalized his BlackBerry. His mind had become one big in-box, and he could not stop himself from opening his mental e-mail at all hours of the day and night. His mind jumped from one demand to the next. He had lost the capacity to relax and simply be present. He was always thinking about whom he needed to contact, what needed to get done, and what could go wrong.

The alarm circuitry in Jerry's brain literally was stuck in the "on" position. If Jerry were a soldier in battle or a firefighter in a burning building, being hyperaroused and hypervigilant might save his life or someone else's. In such a situation, his adrenaline-fueled fight-or-flight response would have genuine survival value. In the context of his work, however, which was not filled with life-and-death danger, his hyperactivated state didn't help to save anyone's life, but it did put his own in jeopardy. For starters, the constant activation of his brain's stress circuitry was taking a toll on his body. With his sympathetic nervous system continually in overdrive, he couldn't get to sleep without drinking alcohol, which is a depressant. When the alcohol wore off a few hours later, he was wide awake again. His adrenal glands attempted to cope with the constant flood of stress hormones by pumping out excess cortisol to preserve his body's energy resources. Unfortunately, a consequence of excessive cortisol is weight gain and insulin resistance, two conditions that were bringing Jerry perilously close to developing type 2 diabetes. In his personal life, his chronically stressed state made him irritable and short-tempered, and as a result he often treated his wife and himself poorly. His moodiness was straining their marriage and putting his health in jeopardy.

I wasn't just being glib when I told Jerry to take a hike. I knew that if we were going to make a dent in his depression in 7 days, he would need to change his brain chemistry and his outlook rapidly. The long, strenuous hike up the mountain would stimulate production of his body's natural antidepressants, including painkilling, euphoria-inducing endorphins; invigorating norepinephrine and dopamine; and calming serotonin. In addition to this potent chemical cocktail, the beauty of the mountains, the camaraderie with the other hikers, the freedom from the to-do list in his head, and the pride in meeting the challenge of the mountain would give Jerry the jump start he desperately needed to climb out of his existential crevasse. I was hopeful that Jerry would experience changes similar to those of the many guests I'd worked with over the years, whose encounters with vigorous, spirited exercise boosted their moods.

Over the past 2 decades, science has caught up with what most people know intuitively: Exercise is a potent antidepressant. A survey conducted by *Runner's World* magazine revealed that the number one reason its subscribers cite for choosing to run is not weight loss or disease prevention—it's the feeling of well-being they get from running. Dozens of studies have shown that aerobic exercise relieves symptoms of depression and that long-term exercise can prevent the recurrence of depression.

A groundbreaking study conducted by James Blumenthal and his colleagues at Duke University in 1999 was the first to compare the impact of exercise on clinically depressed patients with the effect of an antidepressant (Zoloft). I had the pleasure of speaking with Blumenthal when he presented his research as part of a panel I chaired at the Cleveland Clinic's Heart-Brain Summit. The study, cleverly termed SMILE (Standard Medical Intervention and Long-Term Exercise), took place over 16 weeks and included 156 patients. The patients were divided into three groups: Zoloft, exercise, or a combination of the two. The exercise group was assigned to supervised walking or jogging, at 70 to 85 percent of their aerobic capacity (an individual's maximum heart rate in response to intense physical exercise) for 30 minutes three times a week. All three groups experienced a significant decrease in depression, and about half of each group experienced a complete remission of symptoms. Blumenthal's conclusion was that exercise was as effective as medication.

Six months after the study ended, Blumenthal followed up with the patients and found that exercise actually was more effective than medicine over the long term. About 30 percent of the exercise group remained depressed, versus 52 percent of those on medication. Of the patients who were in remission after the initial study, only 8 percent of the exercise group relapsed, versus 38 percent in the medication group.

After the initial 16-week trial period, the study subjects were free to seek further treatment or not. Some chose to enter psychotherapy, some in the medication group started exercising, and some in the exercise group started taking medication, all of which complicates interpretation of the follow-up data. Nevertheless, Blumenthal and his colleagues found that the most potent predictor of whether an individual felt better was how much they exercised. Every 50 minutes of weekly exercise correlated with a 50 percent drop in the probability of being depressed.

This type of dose-response relationship between exercise and depression relief is evident in the rapid improvement many of our guests at Canyon Ranch experience when they begin to exercise. However, it should be noted that many of these depressed guests exercise for several hours every day, much more than the participants in the community-based studies, who typically exercise for 30 to 45 minutes at a time.

Jerry arrived at 8:00 the next morning with sweat running down his face. "Sorry to get your chair all sweaty, Doc. I just got off the elliptical machine." The dark cloud I had seen the day before was beginning to burn off.

"How was the hike?"

"Long! I'm kind of sore today. My quads are not used to all that climbing. You didn't tell me it was 7 miles straight up. The good news is that I slept for 6 straight hours last night. First time I did that in 8 months." He flashed a sheepish smile.

It wasn't long before the changes Jerry was making in both diet and exercise had an impact. Now that he wasn't drinking four cups of coffee and a few glasses of wine each day, his brain was able to get off the adrenaline roller coaster. He was finally able to get the sleep he so desperately needed. Replacing caffeine, alcohol, and junk food with whole grains, vegetables, lean protein, and fresh fruit allowed Jerry's blood sugar level to remain stable and give him a constant supply of relaxed energy. The vigorous physical exercise helped him to release tension and clear his mind. Combined with solid nutrition, frequent experiences of slow belly breathing, and restorative sleep, the exercise helped to boost his supply of serotonin, dopamine, and norepinephrine, his brain's mood-enhancing neurotransmitters. The dark shroud I had seen 5 days earlier was replaced with a healthy glow.

"Did you talk to your wife?" I asked.

"We had a good talk last night," he responded. "No fighting. I thanked her for making me come here. I was way over the edge, and she knew it. I told her I have to find a way to do things differently. She was thrilled, and she wants to help. The only problem is I don't know how to do this in the real world. Monday morning I'm scheduled to fly to Singapore; I have 12 days of client meetings during the day and client dinners at night."

"Do you want to live your life differently?"

"Of course I do. I was dying by inches. I have to change it."

"What would it take to have a life you'd actually like to live?"

"I don't know how to do it. Ever since I was in elementary school, I was an overachiever. Straight A's. Honor roll. After-school jobs. No sports, no dating. Put myself through college and graduate school. I was the brain, the nerd, the fat kid who got straight A's. I learned to ignore my body and just focus on my mind. That was my way to get out of our working-class neighborhood. Dad died when I was 12, and if I was going to get anywhere, I'd have to do it myself."

"You managed to achieve a lot without much support, and you used your mind to do it. What if you valued your body and your heart as much as you valued your mind?"

"What a concept. It seems very foreign."

"You've started doing it here."

"I know. But this isn't real. There are delicious, organic, portioned meals waiting for me in the dining room. There's no access to booze. The fitness instructors just about give me a standing ovation every time I set foot in the gym. My clients aren't calling me every 10 minutes, and I don't have any meetings. Of course I feel great . . . *here*. But my real life is all about deliverables and the bottom line. My clients next week won't be too happy if I tell them we have to cut the board meeting short so I can go hiking."

"No kidding. Whatever you come up with has got to be practical. You've worked with hundreds of companies to develop strategic plans, and you're very good at it. Tonight I'd like you to work on your own strategic plan. It's not rocket science, but it's got to be real and what you're really willing to do for yourself."

Jerry took up my challenge. He came in the next morning with his laptop. "I stayed up last night doing my homework. I'm pretty excited about it." Jerry proceeded to show me a PowerPoint presentation he called "Plan for the Rest of My Life." Complete with photographs and inspirational quotations, it included specific strategies for how he would exercise for 30 minutes every morning, eat three healthy meals, and get at least 7 hours of sleep each night. It also included time for brief breathing and meditation breaks, and ways to connect throughout the day with what he felt grateful for. There were strategies for letting go of anger, frustration, and fear, and a detailed plan for remaining alcohol free for the next 90 days. After the slide show, he clicked on a spreadsheet in which he would keep track of his eating, exercise, sleep, and breathing practices, with spaces to record the results he expected to achieve from these practices. He called it "Jerry: The Spreadsheet."

Jerry also included spaces to record comments about his conversations with his wife and daughter. During his stay he had spoken with them every day, and he looked forward to sharing what he was learning. He was no longer looking at the nightly phone calls as obligatory check-ins, but as a chance to gratefully receive loving support and share his appreciation with his wife.

Jerry left Canyon Ranch 6 pounds and a lifetime lighter than when he arrived. Armed with his spreadsheet and a binder filled with healthy lifestyle information and strategies, he was returning home with cautious optimism.

Jerry and I kept in touch over the following months, and he kept me apprised of his progress, whether he was in Singapore, London, or Scarsdale. He e-mailed a copy of his updated spreadsheet each week, and we spoke periodically by telephone. We met in person when Jerry returned to Canyon Ranch 3 months later. He had dropped a total of 27 pounds and looked 15 years younger. Sporting a T-shirt, khaki shorts, baseball cap, hiking boots, and a huge grin, he looked like a kid on the first day of camp. Greeting me with a big bear hug, he announced, "I'm back!"

"You sure are!"

Jerry was overflowing with enthusiasm, grateful that he had learned how to care for his body before it was too late. He said, "I can't go back, and I need to stay mindful each day to not slip back."

During this visit we focused on improving his relationship with his wife and his daughter, on how to be the husband and father he most wanted to be. He realized that having a more loving attitude with himself and no longer being a slave to his work was enabling him to be more loving with his wife and daughter.

Just as Jerry had always focused intensely on any task he was assigned, he threw himself wholeheartedly into this program, and as a result, his recovery was more rapid and dramatic than what is typical. Many people who engage in a moderate exercise program for the first time experience a more gradual change in mood and energy. The mood-elevating effects of exercise tend to be temporary at first. Soon after beginning an exercise regimen, most people experience an increase in mood-enhancing neurotransmitters, including norepinephrine, serotonin, and dopamine, which provide a mood boost during and for a few hours after a workout. But after a few weeks of consistent exercise, enhanced mood and feelings of well-being tend to become more enduring, as sleep improves, changes in brain chemistry and function occur, and a feeling of accomplishment sets in. In addition to these biochemical changes, 40 different types of endorphins are also released during strenuous exercise, further promoting positive emotions.

Like Jerry, most depressed patients produce an excess of the adrenal stress hormone cortisol, which, over time, causes damage to brain cells and other tissues throughout the body. MRI scans of clinically depressed patients reveal that two parts of the brain, the amygdala and the hippocampus, are especially sensitive to the effects of cortisol. The amygdala is the fear center of the brain;

when you perceive a threat, the amygdala sends out an alarm reaction to other parts of the brain and body to mobilize for action. When the amygdala is constantly activated, a prevailing state of anxiety is created. The hippocampus is part of the brain most involved in short-term memory. In one study, the hippocampi of depressed patients were 15 percent smaller than those of nondepressed subjects. This finding fits with the memory difficulties experienced by many depressed people.

In the past decade, neuroscientists studying brain imaging scans (MRI and PET) made a revolutionary discovery: New brain cells are constantly generated throughout our lives, particularly in the hippocampus. This is a significant finding, as it was once believed that you are born with a fixed number of brain cells—and that they could not regenerate. A hormone called brain-derived neurotrophic factor (BDNF) has been found to increase the creation of these new brain cells and their linkage with existing networks of brain cells. BDNF acts like a fertilizer for new brain cells, which take several weeks to grow and become linked into existing networks of neurons. Scientists studying this process believe it may represent another way in which exercise works to relieve depression. By stimulating the production of new brain cells, exercise helps to counteract the corrosive effect of stress and help the brain to continually create new pathways that help it and you adapt to changing life circumstances. Fresh neural circuitry is able to support new, constructive ways of thinking that replace old, negative patterns of guilt, fear, and helplessness.

The feelings we have about our bodies tend to have a powerful impact on our self-esteem and how we relate to the world. Befriending your body can transform how you feel about yourself and your life.

Within a few weeks of beginning to exercise, my patients feel more relaxed, energetic, and positive about themselves. Each day that they walk, swim, or ride their bicycles brings a feeling of accomplishment that builds self-confidence. They have the energy to tackle new projects at work. They bring more love and enthusiasm to their marriages and their families. As their fitness levels increase, exercise becomes less of an obligation and more of a pleasure, and they begin to accept, respect, and nurture their bodies in ways they previously hadn't.

The emotional transformation brought on by regular exercise is supported by biological and neurological events taking place deep within us. With every step we take, every mile we run, or every lap we swim, we create a symphony of chemical reactions that helps to improve our moods. But if exercise is such a marvelous antidepressant, why don't more people do it? Almost everyone knows that they feel better after exercising, and most of us are well aware of the myriad other health benefits it provides. Exercise should be a no-brainer.

Unfortunately, most Americans don't exercise regularly. Only one in five adults gets the amount of exercise (30 minutes a day, most days of the week) recommended by the American Heart Association, the American College of Sports Medicine, the Centers for Disease Control and Prevention, and the National Institutes of Health. Among those who are depressed, the incidence of regular exercise is even lower. The truth is, most people who are depressed find the idea of summoning the energy to exercise particularly daunting. If you are one of those people, please don't feel guilty or embarrassed. The challenge you are facing is understandable, but it is not insurmountable, and you are certainly not alone. Start small, see what you feel up to today, and build from there. The guidelines in the following chapter can help you create an exercise program that is right for you.

Chapter 3

STARTING AN EXERCISE PLAN

There are many strategies you can use to get started with an exercise program. As you create your exercise plan, consider the following guidelines for putting together a program that you can sustain over the long term.

Choose Forms of Exercise That You Enjoy

If you've always loved the water, make swimming or pool aerobics the centerpiece of your exercise program. If grooving to the beat sets your spirit free, try out a Zumba or salsa class, or simply crank up your stereo and boogie down in your living room. There are hundreds of ways to exercise—the trick is to find a form that you enjoy and make it a consistent part of your life. Whatever you choose should be something you look forward to. If you love doing it, you will be more likely to stick with it—and it will be more likely to boost your mood than an activity you don't enjoy.

Find the Right Environment

This is one of the most crucial aspects of your exercise program. It is important that you exercise in a comfortable and stimulating environment. If you find the gym to be a depressing place, head to your favorite lake, park, stretch of beach, or hiking trail, or simply walk around your neighborhood. The sunlight, the fresh air, and the beauty of the sights around you will make you enthusiastic about exercising and will elevate your mood. If, on the other hand, you love the camaraderie of exercising in a gym, then that's the right place for you.

Make a Schedule and Stick to It

People who are successful at maintaining an exercise regimen create a structured program that fits their schedule. Exercising first thing in the morning is one way to make sure you don't get detoured by other obligations, and you get to enjoy the resulting feeling of aliveness and accomplishment for the rest of the day. But if you are not a morning person, then find the time that works best for you. When it comes to exercise, consistency is much more important than timing. Whatever time of day you choose to exercise, don't let less-important activities—like watching television, making telephone calls, or surfing the Internet—distract you from what may be the most valuable time of your day. If you are convinced that you have too much work to do to have any spare time for exercise, consider that the time you spend exercising will give you more energy, more focus, and more enthusiasm, enabling you to perform at your best and accomplish more in less time.

Get Some Guidance

Many people find it helpful to work with a personal trainer or exercise physiologist who can assess their baseline fitness level, prescribe an exercise routine tailored to their individual needs and goals, and instruct and support them as they get started. Some of my clients who struggle with motivation continue working with their trainers long after they have mastered their workout, solely because they know they will get themselves to the gym if their trainer, whom they are paying, is waiting for them. Most health clubs and fitness centers have professional trainers on staff who can provide guidance and support.

Make It Convenient and Efficient

If you have a demanding career, small children, and aging parents to look after, then 18 holes of golf or months of marathon training may not be in your immediate future. A brisk 30-minute walk during your lunch break may be exactly what you need in the brief amount of time you have available.

The fresh air, sunlight, and aerobic workout of that walk might make it the most valuable 30 minutes of your day. If you live within walking distance of your place of employment, consider commuting on foot. You'll start your workday invigorated, and you'll save money on gas or transit costs to boot!

Be Safe: Don't Overdo It

In selecting your exercise routine, make sure you are physically healthy enough to engage in the type and intensity of exercise you have chosen. Check with your doctor before starting your exercise program, especially if you have a medical condition such as heart disease, diabetes, or high blood pressure.

Choose an activity that is challenging, but not so difficult or exhausting that you get frustrated, risk injury, or give up entirely.

If You Are Achievement Oriented, Set Goals

People who set realistic goals have an easier time sticking with their exercise programs. To be effective, your goals should be observable, measurable, and achievable. For instance, you could set a goal of walking 3 miles in 45 minutes three times a week. After you have achieved that goal, you could increase it to 4 miles in 60 minutes four times a week. The idea is to create goals that are both challenging and realistic for you, so that you feel a sense of accomplishment without feeling overwhelmed.

If You Enjoy Social Activities, Find an Exercise Partner or Join a Group

Many people find that it's more fun and more sustainable to work out with a friend or as part of a group. My mother-in-law, who lives in Iowa, swears that she would not make it out for her daily 7:00 a.m. walk (especially in the middle of February) if her friend Jackie were not waiting for her. Many people enjoy the chance to catch up with friends during a walk or a tennis match. Exercise classes are another great way to connect with others. I love going to my gym and running around the indoor track above the basketball court, where senior citizens take part in a weekly Living Fitness class. It boosts my spirit to see them dancing, skipping, and swaying to the music, with huge smiles on their faces, reaching out and supporting one another in their movements.

Build Some Variety into Your Workouts

Avoid boredom by substituting different activities from time to time. If you have selected a walking program, don't hesitate to substitute a swim, a bicycle ride, or an aerobics video occasionally. The variety will keep your mind engaged, and the cross-training will challenge your body.

If You Are on the Road, Keep Moving

Many people find it harder to maintain their exercise programs when they are traveling. Air travel schedules, changing time zones, irregular work or social commitments, and unfamiliar surroundings all make it tough to maintain your exercise habit on the road. Most hotels have exercise rooms with a treadmill, an elliptical machine, a stationary bicycle, and weight machines, and many have swimming pools. You can always go out for a walk or a jog. It's a great way to see a new place and get your energy flowing after sitting cooped up on a plane, in a car, or in a meeting. On travel days, you can transform the time you spend waiting in airports into walking time.

Savor the Exercise Afterglow

For 2 to 4 hours after you exercise, the levels of mood-enhancing neurotransmitters in your brain and nervous system are at their peak. Many people experience a profound sense of relaxation and well-being during this time. Filled with a powerfully positive feeling that you have generated with your own efforts, you can bask in this exercise-induced glow. In our overscheduled, hectic lives, we often rush from the gym to the car and back to work without having a chance to appreciate how good we feel. Take a few minutes after your workout to soak in the hot tub, sit in the sauna, simmer in the steam room, or just savor a long, hot shower.

Sample Program: Walking

Walking is the most natural physical activity known to mankind. It is a simple and convenient form of exercise that you can do anytime, anywhere. Walking is the perfect way to begin an exercise program, because the risk of injury is minimal and the physical and psychological benefits are enormous. Walking as little as three times a week for 30 minutes each session has been proven to significantly alleviate depression and improve fitness.

Equipment

Minimal equipment is required to start a walking program. Comfortable, weather-appropriate clothing and a pair of supportive shoes are a must. For about $50 to $75, you can purchase good walking shoes that will make your workout much more enjoyable and also help prevent foot, ankle, calf, knee, hamstring, hip, and lower-back problems. Many people also enjoy listening to their favorite music on an iPod or other portable music device while walking.

Finding the Right Environment

If you plan to walk outside, pick a route that is safe and enjoyable. You might walk on a trail, in a park, or through your neighborhood. If the weather is bad or you don't like walking outside, walking indoors is a good alternative. Taking a stroll in the mall or walking on a treadmill is a great way to exercise. If you prefer to exercise at home or simply don't have enough time during the day to leave the office, stash a mini trampoline (about $40) in a closet and walk in place while watching your favorite TV show or during your lunch break. Believe it or not, walking on a mini trampoline is a very good form of exercise. Wherever you choose to walk, make sure that it's an environment that is comfortable for you, where you enjoy spending time. And remember, the faster and more frequently you walk, the greater the physical and psychological benefits you will enjoy, so try to walk at a comfortable but brisk pace.

Proper Walking Form

Walking with good posture significantly decreases the chance of injury and makes walking much easier and more pleasurable. You should stand straight—not rigidly so, but simply tall and relaxed, with your shoulders down and your neck elongated. Your eyes, shoulders, hips, knees, and ankles should all be in line between strides. Keep your head up and your eyes focused straight ahead and concentrate on looking about 15 feet in front of you, with your chin parallel to the ground. Keep your shoulders loose and your arms bent at a 90-degree angle. Your arms should swing close to your torso, and not rise above your chest at the pinnacle of the swing. Step straight in front of you, heel first, with your foot at a 45-degree angle from the ground. Let your weight shift from your heel to your toes, and push off your toes to propel you into your next step.

A Sample Walking Program

Feel free to increase the time you spend on each walk, as well as the number of times you walk per week. Take your current physical condition and your fitness goals into account when constructing your own personalized walking program. Remember: The amount of exercise you get correlates directly with your physical and psychological well-being.

WEEK	DAY 1	DAY 2	DAY 3	DAY 4	DAY 5	DAY 6	DAY 7
1	30			30			30
2	30			30		30	
3	30		30			30	
4	30		30		30		30
5	35		35		35		30
6	35	30			35		35
7	30	35		30	35		35
8	30	35		35	35		35
9	40	35		40	35		40
10	40	40		40	40		40

Reflective Questions

Answer the questions below to get a sense of the kind of exercise program that would be best for you.

1. When I was a child, some of my favorite forms of exercise or active play included:

   _____

   _____

   _____

   _____

2. Currently, I exercise three or more times per week for a period of at least 30 minutes _____ one or two times per week for at least 30 minutes _____ not at all _____

3. My current exercise routine includes:

TYPE OF EXERCISE	TIMES PER WEEK/DURATION (MINUTES)

In addition to my exercise routine, I get some exercise in my daily activities when I:

_____

_____

_____

4. Now that I know that exercise can help improve my mood, I am willing to consider doing the following exercise each week:

TYPE OF EXERCISE	TIMES PER WEEK/DURATION (MINUTES)

5. I notice that after I _____
_____ (*forms of exercise*), I feel:

_____

_____

6. Some of the challenges I face in designing my exercise plan are:

_____

_____

_____

_____

7. I can deal with these challenges by:

_____

_____

_____

_____

8. I will know my exercise plan is working when I reach these
   goals:

   _____

   _____

   _____

   _____

Chapter 4

THE RESTORATIVE BENEFITS OF SLEEP

One of the most powerful ways to enhance your energy and your mood is to get adequate sleep. When you sleep, your body restores itself, replenishing vital hormones and neurotransmitters. If you don't get enough quality sleep for several weeks, you become more vulnerable to depression. In this chapter, we'll explore exactly how sleep, and its absence, affects your mood. You will have a chance to assess your own sleep pattern, discover ways to improve your sleep, and develop a plan for getting adequate rest.

If you have not been getting enough sleep, you are not alone. An estimated 50 million to 70 million Americans don't sleep as much as they should. As noted in the Introduction, over the past 50 years we have been sleeping progressively less, so that today we are sleeping about an hour less per night than we did 50 years ago. The current nightly average for adults is 6 hours and 40 minutes. During that same 50-year period, the rate of depression has doubled every 10 years. The correlation between less sleep and more depression is not a coincidence. Prolonged sleep deprivation can cause mood disturbance. For many years we have known that depression causes problems with sleep. Today we know that the opposite is also true. Sleep problems frequently *precede* the development of a mood disorder.

When we don't get enough sleep, our bodies experience significant changes in levels of neurotransmitters—including serotonin—that make us more vulnerable to depression. Low serotonin levels are associated with feelings of anxiety, irritability, and depression.

A study published in 2007 tested the serotonin levels of night-shift workers (a group that tends to be chronically sleep deprived), compared with those of people who worked during daylight hours. The night-shift workers were found to have significantly lower levels of serotonin than the day-shift workers. Night-shift workers in the study slept on average 1 to 4 hours less than day-shift workers and experienced poorer-quality sleep. This research helps explain why night-shift workers are more prone to depression. Having worked the night shift at a hospital in my early twenties, I can tell you there is a reason they call it the graveyard shift.

Sleep deprivation also activates the body's stress response. One recent study closely observed 26 healthy college students between the ages of 18 and 30 who had either stayed awake all night or gotten a full night's sleep. Their brain activity was monitored by functional magnetic resonance imaging (fMRI) while they were shown a series of 100 photos of images that became increasingly disturbing. The sleep-deprived subjects displayed 60 percent greater activity in the amygdala than their well-rested peers, indicating that they experienced a more powerful emotional response to the disturbing images than the well-rested group did.

The researchers also looked at which brain regions were communicating with one another. In the well-rested subjects, the amygdala seemed to be speaking with the medial prefrontal cortex, an outer layer of the brain that enables us to think calmly about our emotions and put them in context. In the sleep-deprived subjects, however, the amygdala seemed to be "rewired," communicating instead with a brain stem region called the locus coeruleus. The locus coeruleus secretes norepinephrine, a precursor of adrenaline. When your body doesn't get adequate rest, it tends to run on adrenaline. That shaky, jittery, hyper feeling you experience after pulling an all-nighter is actually the body's way of compensating for inadequate sleep.

These studies dramatically illustrate the impact of sleep deprivation on mood and cognitive functioning. Without enough sleep, the amygdala is more reactive to uncomfortable emotional stimulation. And without the emotional regulation provided by the medial prefrontal cortex, the amygdala can hijack the brain and the body, causing heightened anxiety and irritability. If sleep deprivation is prolonged, neurotransmitters that influence mood—such as norepinephrine and serotonin—can become depleted, leading to depression.

So, in the short term, sleep deprivation can make you feel anxious and irritable. You can function during the day, but you tend to feel on edge and emotionally reactive. Prolonged sleep deprivation can also make you feel tired, spacey, and inattentive. If you compensate by reaching for a few jolts of java or caffeinated soft drinks to perk yourself up during the day, you can become even more anxious and may have trouble sleeping at night. Caffeine is a drug that stays active in the body for a long time; that double espresso you have at 3:00 in the afternoon may actually make it more difficult to fall asleep and stay asleep at night. "Treating" your fatigue with caffeine creates a vicious cycle of sleep deprivation and anxiety. Combating your tiredness with a hit of sugar also tends to backfire. The temporary boost of energy it provides is soon followed by a crash that leaves you feeling depleted and craving another junk-food fix. If you eat junk food when you're tired, you'll suffer inflammation and eventual weight gain, as we discussed in Chapter 1.

In the long term (over the course of several weeks), sleep deprivation can cause hormone and neurotransmitter levels to become chronically low, resulting in ongoing feelings of depression. Lack of energy during the day contributes to lower levels of physical activity; this tends to perpetuate sleep difficulties and depression. In addition to the physical effects of sleep deprivation, many people who experience ongoing anxiety, fatigue, and trouble concentrating as a result of inadequate sleep become discouraged, further contributing to their experience of depression.

In order to improve your sleep habits, you must first examine your current sleep pattern. You need to figure out how much sleep you need to feel your best and then do everything you can to make sure you get that sleep. The amount of sleep you need to function optimally is less than it was when you were a child or a teenager. Most adults need 7 to 9 hours of sleep per night, but of course there is individual variation. Some people can get by on 5 hours of sleep, and some need 10.

I want to reassure you that if you occasionally lose a few hours of sleep, you will still be able to function the next day, and you won't sink into depression. Studies have shown that most people can function adequately on 5½ hours of sleep. They may feel irritable, but they are capable of accomplishing the tasks of daily living. Only when sleep deprivation continues for several weeks or more does it pose a serious risk to your mood and your health. It is important to remember this if you are having trouble getting to sleep. You may be able to rest more easily with the knowledge that you will be fine tomorrow even if you miss a few hours of sleep tonight.

Everyone's sleep needs are unique, so the best way to gauge if you are getting enough restorative sleep is to assess your typical level of daytime sleepiness. Because some people are unaware that their depressive symptoms have their origin in sleep deprivation, it is essential that you examine your sleep pattern. When you are getting adequate sleep, you awaken in the morning feeling refreshed, and you are able to wake up without an alarm clock (at a reasonable hour). One sure sign that you are not getting enough sleep is if you feel sleepy during the day.

Take a moment to fill out the following Sleepiness Questionnaire, which will help you assess your sleep pattern.

Sleepiness Questionnaire

How likely are you to doze off or fall asleep in the situations described below, in contrast to simply feeling tired?

Your answers should reflect your typical lifestyle choices. Even if some of the situations below don't apply to you currently, try to estimate how they would have affected you when they were applicable to your life.

Using the scale below, assign the most appropriate number to each situation:

0 = Would never doze
1 = Slight chance of dozing
2 = Moderate chance of dozing
3 = High chance of dozing

SITUATION	CHANCE OF DOZING
Watching TV	
Sitting and talking to someone	
Sitting and reading	
Riding as a passenger in a car	
Driving a car stopped in traffic	
Sitting in a theater or a meeting	
Sitting quietly after lunch	
Lying down to rest in the afternoon	
Total (sum of all 8 ratings)	

If you scored 13 or higher: You definitely are not getting enough sleep.

If you scored from 10 to 12: You probably are not getting enough sleep.

If you scored 9 or lower: You are in the normal range, but it is still possible you could benefit from more sleep. You may be one of those people for whom sleep deprivation results more in anxiety and irritability than in a feeling of sleepiness. You may also be a person who stays busy all day long and thus rarely dozes off even though you are tired and sleep deprived.

If you're not getting enough sleep, there are many possible reasons. You may not be giving yourself adequate time for sleep, or your sleep may be interrupted by factors outside your control, like a crying baby or a snoring spouse. Maybe you give yourself enough time, but you can't fall asleep or you wake up in the middle of the night or early in the morning and are unable to go back to sleep. All of these things happen to most of us at one time or another. But people who are depressed tend to have more trouble getting to sleep and staying asleep than the average person.

If you are sleep deprived because you do not give yourself adequate time for sleep, there are a number of steps you can take right now to increase your sleep and enhance your mood. I have seen international travelers, mothers of young children, and night owls with early-morning job commitments all experience dramatic improvements in their moods once they managed to consistently get more sleep. They made lifestyle adjustments that afforded them adequate time to sleep. In some cases, they needed help from their spouse to tend to their small child in the middle of the night. In others, they needed to adopt a gentler business travel routine or forgo watching late-night TV.

If you have not been giving yourself enough time to sleep, consider the following recommendations:

Value your sleep. Remember, sleep is not a luxury; it is a necessity if you want to stay healthy and perform at (and feel) your best.

Don't stay up late. Some late-evening activities are unavoidable, but many are optional. Watching TV, using the computer, and talking on the phone are definitely optional.

Travel wisely. If possible, choose flights that don't interfere with your normal sleep rhythm. If you have to take an overnight flight, try to sleep on the plane. Many people find that taking melatonin helps them sleep during a long flight. When you arrive at your destination, stay awake all day until your desired bedtime. Spending time outdoors in the sun can also help to reset your biological clock.

Manage your work schedule. If your work schedule interferes with your sleep, do something to change it. If you can't change your work hours, adjust your lifestyle to make sure you get enough sleep.

Keep the kids in their rooms at night. If you have young children, help them learn to sleep in their own beds. Easier said than done, I admit. But the time and effort you invest now will pay dividends in better sleep, mood, and health for you and your child.

Relax at bedtime. Develop a relaxing bedtime routine that lets you wind down and get into bed at your desired bedtime. Your routine might include taking a hot shower or bath, drinking some herbal tea, and reading a chapter of a book.

Take naps. If you are sleepy during the day, and your schedule allows it, take a nap. Avoid napping, however, if you are having trouble getting to sleep at night.

If you have a very busy life and you are wondering how you can find the time to get more sleep, I have a challenge for you: Take 5 minutes to write down a few nonessential activities you could forgo in order to free up more time for sleep. For instance, what if you skipped the news at 11:00 p.m. and went to bed 30 minutes earlier? Would you really miss hearing about disturbing events at the end of your day? Probably not, and you'd sleep better if you spared yourself from violent images before entering dreamland.

Write down three things you would be willing to spend less time on in order to have more time for sleep:

1. _____

2. _____

3. _____

What if you have been giving yourself enough time to sleep, but you are unable to sleep when you want to? You may have insomnia, which includes trouble falling asleep, waking up in the middle of the night, or waking up too early in the morning and being unable to go back to sleep. If you are experiencing insomnia, there are a number of things you can do to improve your sleep. Let's start with the physical and behavioral strategies that tend to promote better sleep.

Maintain a regular sleep-wake schedule. Your body gets used to falling asleep and waking up at certain times. Deviations to that biological rhythm disrupt sleep.

Exercise aerobically most days of the week. Vigorous exercise stresses and warms your body during the day, leading to relaxation and lower body temperature at night, both of which are conducive to sleep.

Avoid exercising 2 to 3 hours before bedtime. Exercising too close to bedtime causes some people to be too alert and activated at bedtime to go to sleep.

Avoid drinking alcohol and eating 2 to 3 hours before bedtime. Although alcohol is a sedative that can promote sleep, its effect wears off during the night and can cause rebound alertness. The activity of digestion can also interfere with sleep.

Avoid caffeine in the afternoon and evening. If you are very sensitive to caffeine, avoid it completely. Watch out for caffeine in coffee, tea, soft drinks, chocolate, and some over-the-counter headache medicines.

Determine if you're taking medication that affects your sleep. Many medications can interfere with sleep, including decongestants, steroids, antihistamines, stimulants, headache medicines, and sedatives.

Make sure your bedroom is cool, dark, quiet, and uncluttered. Most people sleep best in a slightly cool room. If light comes through your window, install blackout shades to make your bedroom completely dark. If you are bothered by noise, consider wearing earplugs or using a white-noise machine or a fan to muffle unwanted sounds.

Use your bed only for sleep and sex. Many people have trouble sleeping because they use their beds for watching TV, working on their laptops, or talking on the phone. You want to condition yourself to associate your bed only with sleep or lovemaking, rather than mentally stimulating activities that promote wakefulness.

What about Sleeping Pills?

Sleeping pills are among the most widely prescribed medications in the United States. Although they are frequently effective in the short term, they can cause serious side effects, and over time they lose their effectiveness. It is not recommended that you take most sleep medications for more than 10 days at a time. Unfortunately many people do, resulting in dependency and the development of potentially dangerous side effects. In addition, while taking sleep medication may help you fall asleep, it does not promote good quality sleep, as sleeping pills disrupt the body's natural sleep cycle. Sleep medicines do not treat the true causes of insomnia. As a result, their effects tend to be temporary, thus perpetuating a vicious and dependent cycle of insomnia and sleeping pills.

Until recently, the most widely prescribed sleep medications were the benzodiazepines. The most popular medications in this class include Klonopin, Ativan, Valium, and Xanax. They induce sleep by depressing brain activity and slowing brain waves. One effect of benzodiazepines is that they cloud our thinking and memory after we take them, which may cause us to forget that we have been awake during the night. This altered sleep perception causes us to overestimate the effectiveness of these sleeping pills, thereby encouraging continued use.

The mind-clouding effect of these medications can also cause a daytime hangover, with impairments in concentration, memory, and mood. They can also impair coordination, making it particularly dangerous to drive a car. Although some people take sleeping pills at night in order to function competently the next day, there is no scientific evidence to support this practice. In fact, the daytime hangover from these medications is often worse than the effects of sleep deprivation. Another problem with benzodiazepines is that they lessen the time spent in deep sleep and dream sleep. As a result, you may get more total minutes of sleep, but it will be lighter and less restorative than natural sleep.

Although benzodiazepines are moderately effective in the short term, over time they become totally ineffective. With continued use, the brain becomes habituated to their effects. There is no scientific evidence that they work for more than 4 to 6 weeks. In fact, the NIH recommends that benzodiazepines should not be prescribed for longer than 2 to 3 weeks.

In the past decade a new generation of sleeping pills, including Ambien, Sonata, and Lunesta, have become extremely popular. These non-benzodiazepine hypnotic sedatives have some advantages over the previous generation of sleep medication: They don't create a daytime hangovers, and they are less likely to be addictive.

But they are still not recommended for use beyond 6 months. In addition, they do carry the risk of dependence and a number of potentially dangerous side effects. Some people have reported experiencing amnesia and erratic behavior after taking Lunesta and Ambien. There have been numerous reports of people binge eating and driving their cars while under the influence of these drugs. People can also experience problems if they do not go to sleep immediately or if they wake up shortly after taking these medications. They may experience dizziness, lightheadedness, impaired coordination, and memory deficits.

Finally, Lunesta, Sonata, and Ambien have been found to increase the risk of depression. Therefore anyone suffering from or at risk of depression should avoid these drugs, since they are more likely to cause depression than to help it. If you are currently taking a sleep medication and want to stop, please consult your doctor, and do not abruptly discontinue use. Most physicians will recommend you slowly reduce your dosage in order to minimize withdrawal symptoms.

Over-the-Counter Sleep Medications

All over-the-counter sleep medications contain an antihistamine called diphenhydramine, known more commonly by its brand name, Benadryl. Although they promote drowsiness, they have not been found to be better than placebos at helping people with insomnia to sleep. In fact, they create anxiety in some people, making it more difficult to sleep. Their many side effects include daytime sedation, impaired memory and concentration, disturbance of dream sleep, tolerance, and psychological dependence.

Herbs and Nutritional Supplements

There are many nutritional supplements that also support healthy sleep. The good news is that they have very few side effects and little risk of dependency. The bad news is that they don't work for everyone. I have found the following supplements, all available without a prescription, to be helpful for many of my patients. Before taking any supplements, be sure to consult with your health care provider.

- **5-HTP:** 5-Hydroxytryptophan is an amino acid that is a precursor of tryptophan, which your body converts into serotonin. As discussed previously, serotonin is a neurotransmitter that induces a feeling of calm and well-being. From serotonin, your body makes melatonin (see next paragraph), a hormone involved in regulating sleep. Since melatonin levels drop as we age, supplementation with 5-HTP can be extremely helpful in improving the sleep difficulties that tend to accompany aging. The few side effects of 5-HTP are generally mild. The most common is stomach upset, which generally disappears within a few days of starting 5-HTP. A dosage of 50 to 150 milligrams in the afternoon and again at bedtime promotes relaxation and sleep.
- **Melatonin:** Melatonin is a naturally occurring hormone secreted by the pineal gland, a pea-size structure located at the base of the brain. Its secretion is stimulated by the absence of light coming in through the eyes. It tends to be released at night when it is dark and when our eyes are closed. Some people find that 1 to 3 milligrams of melatonin 30 minutes before bedtime helps them sleep soundly.
- **Magnesium:** Magnesium is a mineral that promotes relaxation. Since most people are deficient in magnesium, supplementation often helps to enhance feelings of calmness, balance the nervous system, and improve sleep. Magnesium in the form of magnesium citrate or magnesium glycinate is recommended. A daily dose of 400 to 600 milligrams is helpful for overall health and relaxation. An

additional 200 to 400 milligrams at bedtime promotes sleep by further relaxing the nervous system and muscles.

What about Medical Conditions That Affect Sleep?

If you have been struggling for a long time with insomnia that has no identifiable cause, see your doctor to rule out any physical causes of your sleep difficulty. There are a number of medical conditions that can cause insomnia. Blood sugar swings can give you night sweats that interfere with sleep. An overactive thyroid can make it difficult to get to sleep. Adrenal glands that are overactive or release too much cortisol at the wrong time can cause insomnia. Food allergies can interfere with sleep, as can magnesium deficiency. The hot flashes and hormonal fluctuations of menopause can also wreak havoc on sleep. If you do have a medical condition that disrupts your sleep, your doctor may be able to treat your medical condition in a way that affords you better sleep.

Sleep apnea is another medical condition that can dramatically affect sleep and contribute to depression. People with this condition experience intermittent blockage of their airway that can disrupt breathing for up to a minute at a time. Symptoms of sleep apnea include loud, irregular snoring, snorting, and gasping for breath. Sleep apnea patients often feel tired, groggy, and depressed and often suffer from obesity and impaired daytime concentration and memory. If you think you may have sleep apnea, schedule a medical evaluation as soon as possible. Your doctor may refer you to an overnight sleep lab, where you can be tested for sleep apnea. If you do have it, there are a number of interventions that may be helpful, including losing weight, reducing alcohol intake, using a CPAP (continuous positive airway pressure) device during the night, taking decongestant medication, and undergoing surgery.

Relaxing Your Mind and Body for Sleep

Everyone wakes up during the night. Light sleepers wake up more often than sound sleepers and tend to have more trouble getting back to sleep. Sound sleepers wake up for a few seconds and get right back to sleep.

One reason light sleepers have trouble getting back to sleep is that their minds become active when they wake up. They start thinking about daytime concerns, and their bodies react to their thoughts with increased energy and alertness. In addition, when people with sleep difficulties wake up during the night, they often start worrying about whether they will get back to sleep. And then, of course, their anxiety about getting back to sleep prevents them from sleeping.

So, how can you make yourself fall back asleep? You can't *make* yourself go back to sleep. But if your difficulty sleeping isn't the result of a physical condition, the following mind and body relaxation strategies can help sleep come to you.

Ease Your Mind

Remember that nighttime is for sleeping, not thinking. If you find yourself worrying about something, remind yourself that you can think about it tomorrow, during the day. You can think more creatively and constructively during the day, so just set it aside for now. In Chapters 7 to 15, you will find several approaches for dealing with stressful life issues.

Let your mind turn toward things that bring feelings of contentment, rather than concern. Think about the people and things in your life that you appreciate. Remember a pleasant event or envision a beautiful place in vivid detail: a walk in the woods, a garden in bloom, a fabulous movie.

If concerns do enter your mind, don't struggle to resist them. See if you can just observe your thoughts without getting emotionally involved in them. You might imagine they are like clouds floating across the sky or waves rising and falling on the ocean.

Relax Your Body

Shift into slow, rhythmic, belly breathing, inhaling and exhaling through your nose. Allow your abdomen to expand with each inhalation. You could imagine that a big balloon is filling up with air in the center of your body. Imagine you are breathing a soft, soothing feeling of peacefulness into the center of your body. As you breathe out, imagine the balloon deflating as you send that peacefulness into all the rest of your body, including your arms, legs, and head. Allow your breathing to slow down to about three to six breaths a minute. This type of full, slow breathing activates your body's relaxation response and helps you fall asleep. (You can learn more about belly breathing in Chapter 6.)

You can also use acupressure to relieve tension and release your body's natural sleep hormones. First, massage the crown of your head with small circular movements using your index and third fingers for 30 to 45 seconds. Next, using your index fingertips, simultaneously massage the outer ends of both eyebrows at your temples, again for 30 to 45 seconds. Then, rub the palms of your hands together until they feel warm, and gently rest the heels of your hands over your closed eyelids for a minute or two.

Using these relaxation techniques will help to prepare your mind and body for sleep. Even if it takes a little while to fall asleep, this restful time awake will help to balance and replenish your body. If it takes longer than 30 minutes to get to sleep, go into another room and read in low light until you feel sleepy, and then go back to sleep in your bedroom. Remember, if you don't become too worried about being awake, eventually sleep will come.

Lynne's Story

Lynne came to me after she had been suffering from insomnia for 3 months. She was depressed and exhausted from lack of sleep, and was losing weight. She felt guilty about being depressed and irritable around her husband and two daughters, ages 7 and 10, and about missing out on the activities she used to enjoy. Lynne's husband was supportive but felt frustrated with her depression and his inability to help her.

As we worked together, Lynne shared that she frequently awoke during the night with overwhelming feelings of anxiety and regret over something she had said to a friend, acquaintance, or family member. She tended to judge herself harshly after social interactions. After recounting a simple story to a friend, she would often feel overcome with shame and inadequacy. She felt tormented by the afterthoughts that robbed her of sleep, appetite, and peace of mind.

Lynne's fear of making a social misstep was keeping her from interacting with other people. She avoided seeing friends and parents of children in her daughters' classes. She avoided speaking at school meetings for fear that she would say something stupid. Prior to having children, she had worked in a doctor's office, and she missed the stimulation of engaging with other adults. However, Lynne's fear of saying something stupid was ruining her life.

Another significant source of stress for Lynne was her relationship with her mother, who lived alone after the death of Lynne's father several years earlier. Lynne tried her hardest to help her mother, who frequently felt overwhelmed and unable to cope with her own life. While Lynne resented her mother's dependence on her, she also felt guilty that she couldn't do more to ease her mother's pain.

I taught Lynne heart breathing and heart-focused meditation (which are described in detail on pages 105 and 135, respectively). As she used these techniques, she became more skilled at identifying her own critical judgments and finding more compassionate ways to look at herself and her actions. She learned to breathe into her heart when she was in a meeting at her children's school or in a conversation with her mother. If she began to feel upset, she would pause and embrace her distressed feeling, identifying any judgment attached to it. She'd then accept her upset feelings and connect with a feeling of appreciation or contentment. Once she got her emotional bearings, she was able to look at the situation from a calmer place and see it from a fresh, constructive perspective. She also used these techniques at night when she had trouble getting to sleep.

Lynne added some additional relaxing elements to her evening routine to help her sleep. After she put her girls to bed, she took a hot bath, listened to soft music, and did some light reading. She also began taking 5-HTP, which seemed to help calm her nervous system and enable her to stay asleep longer. Within 2 weeks, Lynne was sleeping more soundly, rarely waking up during the night, and feeling more positive and energetic.

Reflective Questions

The questions below will help you assess your current sleep pattern and decide whether your mood might benefit from additional sleep. Some of the questions will help you begin to identify strategies to improve your sleep.

1. I fall asleep easily _____ or with difficulty _____.
2. Throughout the night I sleep completely _____ or erratically _____ or not at all _____.
3. I sleep about _____ hours each night.
4. I am beginning to see that some behaviors or substances (activities, foods, drinks) may be preventing me from achieving restorative sleep. Some of these include:

   _____

   _____

   _____

5. When I wake in the morning, I feel:

   _____

   _____

6. I scored _____ on the Sleepiness Questionnaire. My results indicate:

   _____

   _____

7. I have _____ have not _____ tried prescription sleep medications. I have _____ have not _____ tried over-the-counter sleep aids. I experienced the following helpful _____ unhelpful _____ effects:

_____

_____

_____

8. I have _____ have not _____ tried herbs and supplements to help me sleep. I experienced the following helpful _____ unhelpful _____ effects:

_____

_____

_____

9. I am now using the following techniques to improve the quality of my sleep:

TECHNIQUE	USEFUL	NOT USEFUL

Chapter 5

THE MOOD-
BOOSTING
EFFECTS OF
LIGHT

*Keep your face to the sunshine and you cannot see
the shadow.*

HELEN KELLER

Sunlight brightens your mood. Just about everyone, regardless of
whether or not they suffer from depression, feels better when the
sun comes out. What most people experience intuitively has come
to be understood scientifically in the past 2 decades: Exposure to
sunlight boosts serotonin levels in the brain. Sunlight (or bright
light, to be more exact) is the most abundant and easiest-to-absorb
antidepressant you will find. To receive your daily dose of bright
light, all you need to do is open your eyes. When bright light
reaches the retina, it stimulates the optic nerve, which sends a signal
to the part of the brain that regulates production of serotonin and

melatonin. Serotonin is the same neurotransmitter that is boosted by Prozac, Paxil, and the other selective serotonin reuptake inhibitors (SSRIs). It relieves stressful feelings and produces a general sense of well-being. For depression, bright light works faster than medication, usually within a week, and with fewer side effects. Drugs that boost serotonin generally take 2 to 4 weeks before they begin to work, and in some cases they take as long as 6 weeks.

Bright light has been used as a treatment for winter depression for more than 25 years. Its efficacy in treating winter depression, also known as seasonal affective disorder (SAD), has been supported by dozens of studies. As the days get shorter, cloudier, and colder in the winter months, people with SAD frequently suffer from fatigue, irritability, depression, carbohydrate cravings, sleep problems, and weight gain. Exposure to bright light from the sun or a high-intensity light fixture for 30 to 60 minutes a day is remarkably effective in alleviating the symptoms of SAD.

More recently, at least 15 controlled studies have found that bright light is also an effective treatment for nonseasonal depression. This confirms what I have observed with my clients. In fact, people with a variety of other conditions, including PMS, depression during pregnancy, bulimia, and insomnia, have also shown improvement from exposure to high-intensity light.

For most of human history, people spent almost all of their waking hours outdoors. Our brains and bodies evolved in an outdoor environment bathed in sunlight. Our eyes have special light receptors, connected directly to the middle of the brain, that respond only to the brightness of outdoor light. That light, absorbed by the eyes, stimulates the release of neurotransmitters and hormones that regulate mood, sleep, and energy. Without it, our natural sleep-wake cycle goes awry, and our mood and energy suffer.

As we spend more of our time indoors, we are becoming increasingly deprived of the bright light that is essential to our health and well-being. Many of us are not aware that we are suffering from the effects of light deprivation. Because of our eyes' extraordinary ability to adapt to changes in brightness, we tend not to be aware of how little light we actually receive when we are indoors. Typical indoor lighting is 100 times less bright than outdoor light on a sunny day. Even a cloudy day delivers 10 times more brightness than ordinary indoor lighting.

A recent survey of 1.3 million Americans found that those who live in the sunniest states tend to report the highest levels of happiness. The top seven happiest states in the 50-state survey were all in the Sun Belt (in order): Louisiana, Hawaii, Florida, Tennessee, Arizona, South Carolina, and Mississippi.

The best way to get the mood-enhancing benefits of bright light is to spend at least 30 minutes a day outdoors. Walking outside on a sunny day is an ideal way to combine exercise, light exposure, and the enjoyment of nature. In order to receive the mood-boosting effect, the light needs to be absorbed through your eyes, so do not wear sunglasses. You do not need to look up at the sun. Simply being outdoors will enable you to absorb the light you need.

On a snowy, rainy, cloudy, or very cold day, it may not be practical or possible to get 30 minutes of exposure to bright sunlight. If you can't take in 30 minutes of sunshine outdoors, a high-intensity light box can provide the boost you need.

A high-intensity light box offers a convenient and reliable way to obtain your daily dose of bright light. To receive maximum benefit, you must use a light fixture that provides 10,000 lux of light at a distance of 2 feet. Lux is a measure of brightness. On a sunny day, the brightness of sunlight is anywhere from 10,000 to 100,000 lux (in contrast, typical indoor lighting is only about 100 lux). That's why a high-intensity light box provides such a powerful lift to light-deprived people who spend little time outdoors. It gives them a blast of light that approximates the mood-boosting brightness of sunlight.

There are many high-intensity light boxes available, ranging in price from about $100 to $500. In selecting a model, choose a fixture that has an adjustable stand. The light should be about 18 to 24 inches in front of you. You can set the light fixture on a desk or table so that it's about 6 inches above eye level, shining down into your eyes. This approximates the angle at which outdoor sunlight hits the eyes, and it's the best angle for stimulating the light sensors in your eyes. Do not look directly into the light, as this can hurt your eyes. You can receive your light exposure while you read, work at your computer, or eat breakfast. You can also get your daily dose of light while working out on your treadmill or elliptical machine.

High-intensity light boxes contain fluorescent bulbs, which are cooler and last longer than incandescent bulbs. However, some fluorescent bulbs flutter, which may cause eyestrain and headache. Look for a light box that uses flutter-free technology. An excellent, relatively inexpensive model is the Sunsation by the Sunbox Company. It can be purchased for less than $200. You should also check your health insurance policy, as some insurance providers will cover the full or partial cost of a light box.

Bright Light for Sleep Enhancement

If you are having trouble sleeping, bright light from the sun or from a light fixture may help. Bright light improves sleep by helping to reset your biological clock. When bright light is absorbed through the eyes, it signals the brain to be alert. As you may remember from Chapter 4, darkness stimulates the release of melatonin, causing sleepiness. Bright light, on the other hand, suppresses the release of melatonin. Carefully timed exposure to bright light can help people whose sleep-wake rhythm is out of sync. Those who have trouble falling asleep at bedtime or waking up in the morning benefit from bright light exposure in the morning. Those who wake up too early are helped by bright light exposure in the late afternoon. Just be sure to limit your exposure to bright light within 2 hours of your bedtime, because it can make it difficult to fall asleep.

Side Effects of Light Therapy

Exposure to high-intensity light fixtures has been found to be safe for most people. However, a small minority experience mild side effects. When starting light therapy, it's possible to experience eyestrain, headache, or mild nausea. These symptoms typically disappear within several days as the eyes adjust to bright light exposure. Sometimes moving the light fixture a little farther away or shortening the time of exposure can eliminate the symptoms. Once you are able to tolerate the light exposure comfortably, you can gradually lessen your distance from the fixture and/or increase your length of exposure.

People who have preexisting eye problems, such as retinopathy or macular degeneration, should consult their ophthalmologists before beginning light treatment. Similarly, people who have bipolar disorder should use light therapy only with the supervision of a mental health professional. This is because bright light exposure can, in rare cases, trigger a manic episode.

Some people produce too much serotonin in response to bright light exposure. An excess of serotonin can cause anxiety, jitteriness, or nausea. If you experience any of these symptoms, consult a mental health professional who can guide you in the use of light therapy.

Sunlight and Vitamin D

As I discussed in Chapter 1, long-term exposure to sunlight boosts levels of vitamin D, an essential nutrient in which most Americans are deficient during the fall and winter months. Adequate levels of vitamin D are essential for the healthy functioning of your nervous system and for your mood. Your body needs to absorb sunlight through your skin in order to manufacture vitamin D. That's easy enough in summer months, but can be more difficult in the winter. In addition, winter sunlight does not contain the ultraviolet rays that stimulate vitamin D production. So it may not be possible to get adequate exposure to sunlight in winter. Indoor exposure to a high-intensity light fixture won't help your body make vitamin D, since these fixtures filter out ultraviolet rays. Taking vitamin D supplements is a safe, inexpensive way to make sure you have enough vitamin D. For specific supplement recommendations, turn to page 38.

Reflective Questions

1. When I spend time outside in the sun, I tend to feel:

   _____

   _____

   _____

2. I generally spend _____ minutes a day outdoors.

3. Compared with the rest of the year, in the winter months I tend to feel:

   _____

   _____

   _____

4. Given what I now know about the effects of bright light, I
   expect that increasing my exposure to bright light will:

   _____

   _____

   _____

5. I plan to increase my exposure to bright light by:

   _____

   _____

   _____

6. I do ____ do not ____ intend to use an indoor high-
   intensity light fixture. I plan to use the light fixture for
   ____ minutes a day.

Chapter 6

THE POWER OF BREATH

How you breathe has a powerful impact on your energy, emotions, and health. If you are like most people, you don't think much about your breathing unless you are having a problem with it. Most of the time, breathing happens all by itself, outside of conscious awareness. The moment you pay attention to your breathing, as you may be right now, it comes under your conscious control. When you consciously engage in natural, healthy breathing, it relaxes and energizes you. This is simple to do, but if you are not used to natural, healthy breathing, it will take some practice for it to become easy and familiar. In this chapter I'll explain the dynamics of breathing and teach you several simple, powerful breathing techniques that can reduce your anxiety, increase your energy, enhance your health, and boost your mood.

The body you were born with is perfectly designed for natural, healthy breathing. Your inflatable lungs, flexible chest, strong abdominal muscles, and sturdy diaphragm muscle work in concert to allow for smooth, rhythmic, efficient breathing. The diaphragm, a dome-shaped muscle uniquely designed for breathing, sits below your lungs and above your stomach. It connects with the base of the rib cage in the front, sides, and back of the body. When you breathe in, your diaphragm contracts downward, allowing your lungs to expand. When you breathe out, your diaphragm relaxes and recoils upward, thereby decreasing lung volume. Natural, healthy breathing gives you an immediate feeling of relaxed well-being. The efficiency of this breathing also bestows a long-term health benefit: Natural, healthy breathing provides more oxygen with less effort, allowing for optimal oxygenation of the brain and tissues throughout the body.

If you're like most people who have not yet learned natural, healthy breathing, you probably don't breathe as smoothly and easily as you could. That's because most of us developed patterns of muscle constriction early in childhood that continue to inhibit our breathing. It seems paradoxical that so many people have trouble with a process as natural and essential to life as breathing.

If we look at how a child develops, we can see exactly how breathing can become inhibited. One of the biggest challenges for a young child is learning to regulate his or her emotions. How do you stop crying when your mother leaves you in your own bed at night? How do you handle the pain of falling as you struggle to walk? Or the recurring frustration of being told "no" dozens of times a day? Such are the challenges of childhood, and we all had to find ways to handle them.

One of the ways you learned to manage your emotions was by tensing the muscles in the core of your body. You found you could suppress that flood of feeling welling up in the center of your body by tightening your chest and belly muscles. Tightening muscles in the core of your body restricts the flow of energy and emotion, and protects you from feeling uncomfortable emotions. Muscular constriction inhibits your experience of internal space and keeps strong feelings under wraps. It also restricts your breathing.

Over many years, constricted breathing becomes habitual. Tight muscles around the rib cage and abdomen prevent the diaphragm from moving freely. Breathing with tight muscles tends to be shallow and inefficient. Inefficient breathing requires a faster rate of breathing to meet the body's oxygen needs. With rapid breathing, heart rate increases, neck and shoulder muscles also become tense, and the body's stress response is activated. As a result, people who engage in constricted breathing are more prone to experience anxiety and stress-related conditions such as hypertension, headaches, and depression. Over time, constricted breathing also drains energy, resulting in feelings of fatigue and lethargy.

The good news is that with a little training, you can learn simple ways of breathing that can transform your health and well-being for a lifetime. Breathing freely can increase energy, decrease anxiety, and enhance mood very quickly. Shifting from constricted breathing to relaxed, natural breathing turns off the body's fight-or-flight stress response. This balances the autonomic nervous system, producing a feeling of relaxed energy, mental clarity, and a physiological state that promotes health and vitality.

Rather than *inhibiting* your experience of internal space in your chest and abdomen, you can learn to *inhabit* it. In doing so you will allow your emotions and energy to flow freely. Unrestricted breathing literally opens up the space within you and inspires you with the energy of life.

Opening up to healthy breathing is one of the fastest ways to transform how you feel and how your body functions. Many of the people I work with are amazed to find how quickly healthy breathing brings them into a state of balanced relaxation. With the help of medical biofeedback instruments, I am able to show them how breathing can regulate their heart rate, adrenaline level, muscle tension, and bloodflow. When they see this computer-generated data, it confirms what they already sense intuitively. Breathing powerfully transforms their physiology.

In the pages that follow, I will describe seven different types of breathing exercises, each of which yields a specific result. Some of these may be better choices for you than others, depending on your mood. You can experiment with each of them and find the methods that most benefit you.

Belly Breathing

Belly breathing involves the relaxation and contraction of the abdominal muscles. As you inhale, your abdominal muscles relax. Your diaphragm lowers and your lungs expand into the space created by the lowering of your diaphragm. Your abdominal muscles contract as you exhale. Your diaphragm rises, causing the space in your chest to shrink and your lungs to deflate.

Try This

Close your eyes and imagine a balloon in the center of your chest and abdomen that inflates when you inhale and deflates when you exhale. Take a few slow, deep breaths as you continue to imagine the balloon inflating and deflating.

What sensations did you experience in your chest and abdomen?

How did you feel throughout your body after taking a few of these breaths?

Follow these steps to engage in slow belly breathing:

1. Sit comfortably in an upright chair or lie on your back on the floor.
2. Place your hand over your abdomen.
3. Begin by exhaling deeply and fully through your nose. Feel your abdomen contract as you actively exhale.
4. Inhale gently through your nose, allowing your belly to expand (feel it expand outward toward your hand).
5. Exhale softly, contracting your belly (feel it contract).
6. Continue breathing slowly and deeply. Let your breathing be gentle rather than effortful.

7. You may notice a slight pause at the end of the exhalation, before each inhalation. You can relax in the pause.

8. Enjoy the feeling of opening up to each new inhale and the relaxation that comes with letting go of the exhale.

9. Do this for 10 to 12 breaths and then go about your daily activities.

10. Take a few minutes during your day (perhaps once in the morning and once in the evening) to practice this technique.

11. Shift into a few slow belly breaths any time you want to reduce tension and stress and enter into a calmer state of mind and body. You can do this while waiting in line at the supermarket, using your computer, or lying in bed.

This simple change in breathing affects your mind as well as your body. From a calmer place, you are able to access your inner wisdom and respond thoughtfully to people and situations you encounter. Taking the time to slow down and relax has a dramatic effect on your physiology and your possible interpretations of the events going on around you. After just a few minutes of natural belly breathing, a powerful chemical message is sent to the body to slow down and relax, reducing the level of adrenaline in your bloodstream. You will begin to feel refreshed, calm, and even peaceful. You'll have more insight into the present moment, and you will be more in control of your responses to others.

Resonant Breathing

Resonant breathing involves rhythmic belly breathing at a specific rate of inhalation and exhalation. As you inhale, your heart rate speeds up, and as you exhale, your heart rate slows down. When you breathe this way at the rate of six breaths per minute, your physiology enters a profound state of balance.

Follow these steps to engage in resonant breathing:

1. Begin by engaging in slow belly breathing.
2. *Inhale slowly,* expanding the abdomen, as you count to five.
3. *Exhale slowly,* contracting the abdomen, as you count to five.
4. Repeat this for a full minute. At the end of 1 minute, you will have taken six full breaths.

One full breath is defined as an inhale and an exhale. This means that one breath takes 10 seconds, evenly distributed over the inhale and exhale. Biofeedback studies have demonstrated that at the rate of six breaths per minute, the heart becomes entrained, or synchronized, with the breath and signals the brain to release serotonin, endorphins, and dopamine, the "feel-good" neurotransmitters. Breathing at six breaths per minute is called resonant breathing because a specific type of tissue in the heart (called the baroreceptor) actually resonates or vibrates when synchronized to the breath.

You may find it beneficial to work with a biofeedback specialist when you try resonant breathing. While the six-breaths-per-minute respiration rate is an average that applies to most people, we all have individual physiologies that may be slightly different—yours may be between five and seven breaths per minute.

If you practice resonant breathing daily, you will strengthen your body's capacity to produce feel-good neurotransmitters on an ongoing basis. Resonant breathing provides you with a sense of balance, enabling you to be resilient and resourceful in the face of stressful circumstances.

Heart-Centered Breathing

Heart-centered breathing is another breathing practice that uses the physiological balance of rhythmic belly breathing and adds an intentional emotional focus. When you breathe in a rhythmic, resonant pattern, the resultant biochemical release helps you feel better, more relaxed, and more positive. These emotions are side effects of the breathing practices themselves. In heart-centered breathing, you take a more active approach. You directly cultivate the emotions of appreciation and love.

Follow these steps to engage in heart-centered breathing:

1. Begin with belly breathing, adding a few moments of your resonant breathing pattern if you wish.
2. After about 2 minutes of breathing in this fashion, bring your focused attention to the area around your heart. Visualize a person in your life from whom you have felt a great deal of love and trust. Imagine feeling the love and appreciation flowing directly into your heart now, as you are breathing. Allow your gratitude for this person to fill your mind and your heart.
3. Stay with your breathing and the emotions of love and appreciation. Now let the face of that person gently fade away so that only the feelings of love, appreciation, and gratitude remain. These are gifts that reside deep within you, available for you to experience whenever you wish.

When you combine belly breathing with a thought that evokes a nourishing feeling, such as love or appreciation, you will find that you are better able to tolerate negative emotions and cultivate ongoing feelings of well-being.

The Ocean (or Three-Part) Breath

The ocean breath relaxes and energizes your mind and body. When you are feeling anxious or are having negative thoughts, the ocean, or three-part, breath is an excellent technique for managing these emotions. You can use it to balance your autonomic nervous system and "check in," examining your thoughts and assessments before they take over your day.

Follow these steps to engage in the ocean breath:

1. Begin by noting how you feel in your body. Are you comfortable or uncomfortable? What specifically feels uncomfortable? What emotion or mood accompanies this sensation of discomfort? Jot down this information on a piece of paper.

2. Observe the pattern of your thoughts. Are they positive, hopeful, and forward-thinking? Are they negative, hopeless, and stuck? On the same piece of paper, write down the *pattern*, but not the content, of your thoughts.

3. Now sit upright in a comfortable position. Close your eyes and notice your breathing. Is it full or shallow? Is your belly or your chest rising and falling?

4. Now, breathing through your nostrils, begin your next inhale by expanding your lower abdomen to the count of 3 full seconds, then expanding your navel area to the count of 3 full seconds, then finally expanding your upper chest to the count of 3 full seconds. Exhale slowly, through your mouth, to the count of 6 full seconds.

5. Continue your ocean breathing for 5 minutes.

When you are finished, notice how you feel in your body. Are you uncomfortable or comfortable? What is the emotion, sensation, or mood you are feeling now? Jot this information down on your piece of paper. Take a moment to compare how you were feeling before you practiced the ocean breath and how you feel afterward. Each time you engage in this type of breathing, observe the impact it has on your mood and your energy.

The Energy-Transfer Breath

The energy-transfer breath is more of a technique than a practice, and it helps to alleviate anxiety and depression. When we feel anxious, we are generally preoccupied with worry about events that have not yet happened. Our body's fight-or-flight stress response is continually activated, flooding our bloodstream with adrenaline. Our heart rate accelerates, our muscles tense, and our breathing becomes short, shallow, and fixated on the movement of the upper chest. Ongoing anxiety often results in chronic muscle tension. Anxious people often report headaches, neck and shoulder pain, and lower-back pain.

When we are depressed, we tend to focus our thoughts repetitively on negative assessments of our current situation or depreciatory views of ourselves. These negative thought processes directly affect our bodies. Our bodies live in the stories we create about our lives.

Depression is often an indication that we have "worn out" our fight-or-flight reaction and our bodies are having a difficult time manifesting the energy required for motivation, action-oriented thoughts and decisions, or a sense of positive well-being. Depressed people often report low energy, irritability or touchiness, and a sense of paralysis; their muscles just don't seem to respond to the prospect of movement. Depressed people are stuck in chronic deactivation.

The energy-transfer breath can help to resolve both the issue of overactivation and that of deactivation.

Follow these steps to engage in the energy-transfer breath:

1. Begin with belly breathing. Continue this practice for 5 minutes.
2. Mentally scan your body and identify which parts of you feel the most relaxed.
3. Imagine the calm, flowing energy contained in the relaxed parts of your body is now flowing into the parts of you

that are the most stressed, tense, uncomfortable, painful, or run down. You can imagine that the flowing energy has a color, a texture, or a shape. For instance, you could experience a soft violet mist flowing through your body. Or you could experience the calm energy as a warm golden liquid or a fragrant stream of rose petals. You can imagine that your breath is sending the calm energy through your body to the parts that need it most.

Here is an example of the energy-transfer breath in action. Raymond feels completely unable to get up and participate in his family's activities. He sits slumped in a chair while everyone else is actively getting ready to attend an exciting event. He may even be thinking of excuses to get out of this family obligation. He begins to notice that his body feels sore and overwhelmed. Rather than devise an excuse that will disappoint his family, he decides to try the energy-transfer breath.

After a few minutes of belly breathing, Raymond begins to scan his body, looking for an area that seems energetic and activated. Beginning with the top of his head, he consciously scans to the area of the neck and shoulders, then from the shoulder area to the hips, then from the hips to the bottoms of the feet. He notices an area of relaxed, flowing energy in his upper body, and then visualizes that energy flowing down into his legs, which previously felt stuck in the "off" position.

As he visualizes this flow of energy, he begins to flex and move his upper thighs and then move his ankles around in a circular motion. As his body reclaims its capacity to move, Raymond's mind is able to consider the possibility of joining his family.

Overcoming depression is possible through a series of small, deliberate steps just like this one. The energy-transfer breath can be used again and again to remind the body and mind that movement is associated with positive thoughts. You do not have to have grand thoughts or magnificent expectations to manage a depressed mood. You only need to feel good enough to "join in." Developing the capacity to positively transform negative emotions and moods, as well as to create an instant physiological shift, provides an empowering sense of control that helps eradicate the feeling of helplessness that often accompanies depression.

The Breath of Fire and the Breath of Joy

The breath of fire and the breath of joy are two extremely powerful breathing practices that energize the entire body and open the mind to a radiant awareness of joy. Often we are so preoccupied with daily living or so captivated by the belief that our happiness is based on what we have or do not have, that we are unaware that a sense of aliveness and joy can be produced without an objective cause or circumstance. The breath of fire and the breath of joy offer two ways to raise your energy level, enhance your mood, and lift your attitude.

These breathing practices directly invigorate your nervous and glandular systems, prompting endocrine secretions that cleanse and purify the body. They not only revitalize your body, they permeate your mind with an inner experience of joy. This joyfulness weaves through all realms of mood, thought, feeling, and sensation. You cannot help but smile, laugh, or open your mind to creative possibilities.

Happiness, it seems, is independent of outer circumstances. This fiery joy shakes your former perceptions and beliefs to the ground— you realize that you are not powerless. In the face of this awareness, any anxiety you are experiencing about future events becomes irrelevant. Who can worry about what has not happened? Your feelings of joy help you release the need to affect events beyond your control. An extraordinary sense of aliveness dissolves feelings of inertia and helplessness. This intense personal experience quickly spills over and makes it easier to engage with others as well.

Follow these steps to engage in the breath of fire:

1. Begin with a few minutes of slow belly breathing. Focus your attention on the sensation of stretching and collapsing your abdomen as your belly moves with each inhales and exhale. Let your inhales become a little quicker and shorter as your exhales become a little more forceful.
2. Now speed up the inhale and exhale a little more with each breath until you achieve a comfortable rhythm. Keep your focus on the expansion and contraction of your belly muscles.
3. Notice that only your abdomen is moving; your shoulders, neck, and upper chest should remain still and relaxed. Develop a comfortable rhythm of breathing.
4. If you find yourself feeling dizzy or breathless, you've probably lost your abdominal focus and are breathing with your upper chest, activating your body's fight-or-flight response. If this happens, slow down and refocus on slow, belly breathing and begin to accelerate your breath of fire again.

The breath of joy combines deep breathing with fluid arm movements to intensify the flow of energy throughout the body. The arm motions help to fill the lower, middle, and, finally, the upper lungs. Try to let the breath guide your movement, keeping the motions fluid and rhythmic. Flexing your knees causes a slight bounce that protects your lower back. If you have lower-back problems, you can do this technique with less movement of your torso.

Follow these steps to engage in the breath of joy:

1. Begin by standing with your knees slightly bent and your feet hip-width apart. Keep your knees soft to protect your lower back.

2. Exhale fully. Then, as you inhale, raise your arms straight in front of you with your palms down. Allow your knees to straighten slightly with the movement. As you continue inhaling, swing your arms down slightly and then out to the sides to shoulder height. Finish your inhalation as you raise your arms overhead, with your palms facing each other.

3. Swing your arms downward in front of you as you exhale with a full-throated "ha" sound. Bend forward at the hips and let your momentum carry your arms behind you. The motion should be smooth and effortless, keeping your focus on your breath.

4. Inhale as you bring your torso upward, raising your arms in front of you, immediately beginning a second repetition. Swing your arms out to the sides, and then lift them overhead, again exhaling with the sound of "ha."

   Repeat this entire sequence 10 times.

You can use these two breathing practices whenever you wish. They can be especially helpful in the morning to energize and enliven you. As you raise your arms in the breath of joy, you can imagine welcoming the new day with a spirit of openness and gratitude. If you suffer from depression, the breath of fire and the breath of joy can be used daily to break up patterns of blocked energy and negativity, and to boost your ability to generate positive feelings.

In a very short period of time, people who practice these different forms of breathing feel better, less anxious, and more energetic and engaged in their own and others' lives. How you breathe affects the moods, thoughts, and story in which your body is living. When you change your breathing, you change the story of your life.

An Overview of Breathing Practices

TYPE	BENEFITS	WHEN	
Belly Breathing	Quickly shifts us out of fight-or-flight mode.	Transition at the end of a stressful event; regular check-in to reduce stress.	
Resonant Breathing	Balances the autonomic system and influences release of positive neurotransmitters and biochemicals.	Daily on a regular basis, to help keep "feel-good" neurotransmitters flowing.	
Heart-Centered Breath	Cultivates the emotions of self-love and self-appreciation.	Daily, to counteract automatic negative thoughts.	
Ocean (Three-Part) Breath	Provides relaxation, energy, and balance.	Any time you notice fatigue, anxiety, or negative thinking.	
Energy-Transfer Breath	Relaxes tense or painful areas of the body.	Any time negative thoughts have resulted in bodily tension.	
Breath of Fire	Energizes the entire body with vitality.	Any time you wish to increase energy and heighten feelings of vitality.	
Breath of Joy	Energizes the body with streaming energy and a radiant feeling of joy.	Any time you would like to increase energy and experience joy. Especially helpful to get energy flowing in the morning.	

HOW
Expand your abdomen as you inhale, and contract your abdomen as you exhale.
Using the belly breathing pattern, inhale slowly for 5 full seconds, and exhale slowly for 5 full seconds.
Begin with belly breathing. Bring your attention to your heart, visualize a person or being who has offered you unconditional love, then allow the feeling of appreciation to flow in as you inhale and flow out into the world as you exhale.
Inhale, first expanding your abdominal area, then expanding your navel area, then expanding your upper chest.
Begin with belly breathing. After 5 minutes, identify the most relaxed area of your body (it could even be your brain), then imagine the calm, flowing energy contained in this area traveling to the part of you that is most stressed, tense, uncomfortable, painful, or run down.
Begin with slow belly breathing. Focus attention on the sensation of filling and emptying your abdomen as your belly moves with each inhale and exhale. Let your inhales become a little quicker and shorter as your exhales grow a little more forceful. Now speed up the inhale and exhale more with each breath until you achieve a comfortable rhythm, all the while keeping your focus on the expansion and contraction of your belly muscles.
Amplify breath awareness with arm swings synchronized with inhalation and exhalation.

Reflective Questions

Take a moment to answer the following questions, which will help you gain a deeper understanding of the effectiveness of each of these breathing techniques for your mind and body.

1. When I am upset or bothered, I notice I breathe in the following way:

   _____

   _____

2. When I practice breathing by imagining a balloon inflating in my chest and abdomen, I notice:

   _____

   _____

3. When I practice the following breathing techniques, I notice:

TECHNIQUE	EFFECTS
Belly Breathing	
Resonant Breathing	
Heart-Centered Breathing	
Ocean, or Three-Part, Breath	
Energy-Transfer Breath	
Breath of Fire	
Breath of Joy	

4. I feel the most energized when I engage in the following
   breathing practices:

   _____

   _____

   _____

   _____

5. I realize I can feel better by noticing how I am breathing in
   the moment, then switching to the _____
   form of breathing.

6. I am finding that practicing the _____
   _____ form of breathing for ____ minutes
   ____ times a day helps to improve my mood.

PART II

WORKING WITH YOUR MIND

In Part I we focused on physical ways to boost your mood. Nutrition, exercise, sleep, exposure to light, and breathing exercises engage the body to replenish your energy and lift your spirits. In this part of the book, I invite you to focus on the mind. How you pay attention, handle your emotions, think, and the things you choose to focus on all have a powerful impact on your overall mood and energy level. In the coming chapters you will learn how to understand your thoughts and feelings from a new perspective. This perspective offers an expanded understanding of who you are and the role of your thoughts and feelings in your life. The mental strategies presented in Part II will help you lift your mood and move toward a more satisfying and vital future.

The rest of our work together may feel more subtle than what we have done so far. Eating, exercise, breathing, and sleep are all fairly tangible and observable activities. From this point forward, we'll talk about what you are thinking and feeling, your awareness of the present moment and of yourself, and the choices you make about what is most important to you. Some of the ideas I present may seem a little challenging at first. Hang in there. As you try out the exercises and each concept becomes more familiar, you will begin to experience the healing potential they offer.

Here's a basic overview of the principles in Part II.

- Living in the present moment with nonjudgmental, open-hearted acceptance puts you in touch with a tremendous source of vitality. Your life is happening only in the present, and you can learn to strengthen your capacity to *really live* there.
- Unleashing the energy that comes from living in the present means *feeling* your feelings—wholeheartedly and without defense. Joy, pain, anger, love, sadness, hope, gratitude: This is not for the fainthearted. Befriending your feelings

takes skill and courage. By engaging in the practice of
present moment awareness, you can cultivate both of these
qualities.

- As you practice presence, you will overcome the avoidance of
feelings and experiences that is characteristic of depression.
As you engage more fully with life, you will also break free
of the depressing grip of rumination. Becoming more present
allows you to cultivate a wise and compassionate center of
awareness from which to experience your life.

- Living fully in the present also involves understanding how
your thoughts color your moment-to-moment experience.
You can learn to identify and transform the negative thinking
that constricts your energy. When you can relate to your
thoughts as just thoughts and not necessarily facts, you
gain tremendous freedom.

- As you witness and free yourself from the pull of your own
thoughts, you develop the Observing Self, a rich source of
wisdom. You will deepen your connection with this part of
you that is conscious of every aspect of your experience. It
is more than the combination of your thoughts, feelings,
and physical sensations. Your Observing Self enables you
to be aware of all of the *contents* of your experience, and it
is the vantage point from which you experience your life
unfolding. Because it is conscious of every aspect of you, it
provides a deep source of wisdom. It enables you to
embrace your emotions compassionately and defuse the
myriad negative thoughts that arise in your mind.

- You can consciously cultivate qualities that nourish your
inner life and energize your actions. You can fortify
yourself with forgiveness and gratitude.

- The intuitive skills you are cultivating can be used to
confront situations that you want to change. When you

decide to confront an issue that needs to change, you
mobilize a powerful source of energy.

- Identifying and acting in alignment with your deepest values
  unleashes a source of vitality. When you identify what is
  important to you, you can make a plan and take action.
- You can use the strategies and tools offered in this program
  to develop the skill of resilience—the capacity to handle
  whatever challenges life brings.

Chapter 7

MAINTAINING PRESENCE

I don't believe people are looking for the meaning of life as much as they are looking for the experience of being alive.

JOSEPH CAMPBELL

A willingness to experience both your interior and exterior worlds openheartedly is a potent antidote to depression. Tuning in to your moment-to-moment experience, without avoidance or distraction, connects you with a feeling of aliveness, or vitality. This practice, called presence, is at the heart of *The Mind-Body Mood Solution*. The vitality that results from the practice of presence is a rich source of energy that dissolves the constricting, deadening effects of depression. Like the morning sun that burns away the fog, presence enlivens you and allows you to see the world and yourself more clearly.

Before we go on, I need to mention that practicing presence may be challenging at first. The very nature of being depressed can make it difficult to engage fully with the present moment. If you are depressed, it may be hard for you to concentrate, experience pleasure, and feel your emotions fully. Your mind may generate a running commentary of judgments that distracts you from what is actually happening *now*. You may ruminate about past mistakes and worry about future troubles.

Don't give up! In spite of these challenges, and in fact *because* of them, practicing presence can help you overcome depression. By purposely, openheartedly, and nonjudgmentally paying attention to what you are experiencing in the present, you will be open to what Joseph Campbell describes as the "experience of being alive." As you practice presence, you will be able to savor the richness of what you see, hear, feel, taste, and smell. You will become aware of the full range of your emotions. You will develop a nuanced understanding of how your mind generates thoughts and how those thoughts color your reality. And, most important, you will learn that you are more than the sum of these parts. You are more than the sensations, emotions, and thoughts that you experience. You are the expansive consciousness aware of all of those experiences. When you stay in touch with that awareness, your *experience of being alive* will become increasingly rich and vital.

Being present involves feeling the full range of your emotions with conscious awareness. This means feeling anger and sadness as well as peacefulness and joy. *All* of your emotions—even the ones that don't feel good—are a source of energy and self-knowledge. Presence involves paying attention to your emotions, learning from them, and not suppressing them. With clear awareness you are free to *respond thoughtfully* to your emotions rather than *react reflexively* to them. Instead of reacting in old conditioned patterns, you are able to be in touch with a deeper source of wisdom.

One rainy afternoon in 1980, a man I've never met expressed a depth of wisdom that deeply touched me. My wife had been driving alone on a busy highway that day, and came upon a line of cars that had suddenly stopped. When she braked, her car began to skid on the rain-soaked road. Rather than hit the car in front of her, she ran into the cement barrier to her left. The two tires on the driver's side climbed the median, and then the car careened on its other two tires across three lanes of traffic. Balanced on two tires, it was heading toward a 40-foot drop to another highway below. As it reached the right-hand lane, her car collided with and badly damaged a gray Mercedes. Both cars came to a grinding halt next to the restraining railing.

A man emerged from the driver's side of the Mercedes and approached my wife's car. His wife and three children inside his car were all unharmed. He opened the door, helped my wife to her feet, and asked if she was injured. She replied that her only injury seemed to be a sprained ankle. The words he uttered next would stay with my wife and me forever. With a look of utmost compassion, he told her: "If I was ever going to be in an accident, this is the one I would want to be in. Because if I had not been there, you would not be here now."

Imagine the terror he must have felt moments before as he saw a car coming toward him and his family. And imagine again how he may have felt seeing the damage done to his Mercedes. Another man might have reacted out of anger or fear. Somehow his response came from a place of wisdom and an awareness of the preciousness of life. All of us have that potential to act from a place of wisdom, even though we may not always be in touch with it. And we are certainly able to develop this wisdom and awareness and express it more fully as we live our lives.

In the book *Man's Search for Meaning*, Viktor Frankl discusses how he found the strength to endure the horror of life in a Nazi concentration camp. He describes the personal freedom and power that come from understanding that it is the way we choose to respond to a situation, and not the situation itself, that determines our ability to endure it. No matter what you are faced with, there is a gap between it (the stimulus) and your response to it. In that gap between the stimulus and your response is where you have the freedom to make a conscious choice. You are not *controlled by* the stimulus. You control your response to the stimulus.

Becoming familiar with the gap between stimulus and response and learning to inhabit it with wisdom and compassion is a great source of freedom. While you may not be able to control the events you are confronted with, you can certainly be aware of your automatic reactions to them and make conscious choices about how to respond.

One of the benefits of practicing presence is that it frees you from getting stuck in your own thoughts. Practicing presence helps you become aware of your thoughts and feelings without becoming enmeshed in them. You can allow your thoughts to be present as thoughts, your feelings to be present as feelings, without needing to control or eliminate them. Compassionate, nonjudgmental awareness allows you to make peace with yourself.

What I call presence is similar to an approach known as mindfulness. It is central to a number of schools of therapy, such as Dialectical Behavior Therapy, Acceptance and Commitment Therapy (ACT), and Mindfulness-Based Cognitive Therapy. In recent years, health care practitioners have increasingly recognized the benefits of mindfulness. Doctors and therapists are referring their patients for mindfulness training to help them cope with anxiety, depression, and a wide array of medical conditions. This approach has been shown to be helpful in coping with chronic pain and in reducing symptoms of psoriasis, high blood pressure, and immune system disorders. Women struggling with infertility experience higher rates of conception after participating in an 8-week mindfulness program at the Deaconess Hospital in Boston. Practicing mindfulness has also proven helpful for patients seeking to lose weight and overcome drug and alcohol addiction.

The transformative power of presence has been understood and practiced for millennia. Because the experience of presence enlivens our connection to all of life, it is at the core of many spiritual and religious traditions. As we develop the ability to be fully present, we become more connected to ourselves, to others, and to the larger world.

While the practice of presence sounds simple, it is actually complex and at times challenging. It requires ongoing practice to develop the emotional and cognitive skills involved in the experience of presence. Later in this chapter, you will have opportunities to engage in exercises that help you cultivate these capacities. You will get the most out of this program if you practice the exercises, rather than just read them. Even though they may feel awkward at first, your practice of presence will gradually become second nature to you. As the practice of presence becomes natural, you and your life will be transformed.

You have experienced presence before. We all have moments of presence. Think about a time when you felt fully alive, a time when you were completely absorbed in what you were experiencing and consciously aware that you were absorbed in the moment. Presence is a natural capacity that is always available to us. By choosing to practice presence, you become open to the possibility of living an awakened life.

Present Moment Awareness

Life can only be experienced right now. The past is gone and the future hasn't yet happened. Here and now is where the action is. When you are fully present, fully awake to life, you and your life become infused with vitality.

If you are like most people in our modern culture, you probably don't spend much of your waking life fully engaged in the present. Like the rest of us, you possess the uniquely human ability to reflect on the past and imagine the future. Our capacity to conceptualize the past and future has enabled us to learn from experience, invent, create, plan, and maintain our position comfortably at the top of the food chain. Unfortunately, our capacity to think about the past and the future is a double-edged sword: It allows us to be extraordinarily successful and immeasurably miserable. Our ability to ruminate on the past and worry about the future opens us up to considerable suffering. If you have ever lain awake at 3:00 in the morning plagued by thoughts that you can't get out of your head, you know exactly what I mean. Mark Twain perfectly described the cost we pay for our imaginative minds: "I've seen a heap of trouble in my life and most of it never came to pass."

Practicing presence does not mean that you have to completely banish thoughts about the past or the future. That kind of connection to the present might work for your cat, but it doesn't work for you. Rather, the aim of presence is for you to be able to shift intentionally and flexibly from present moment awareness to thinking about the past or future. The idea is to be fully conscious of what you are experiencing right now, whether it is an immediate sensory experience, a memory, or a fantasy about the future.

Coming to Your Senses

One of the best ways to experience the present moment is to *taste* it. Your senses, including your sense of taste, bring you into contact with the present moment.

I first experienced the following exercise during a mindfulness meditation retreat led by Jon Kabat Zin, PhD, a teacher and researcher who has pioneered the use of mindfulness training in clinical settings for stress reduction and health promotion. In this exercise, you will have an opportunity to be fully present to a raisin. If you're like most people, you usually grab a handful of raisins and pop them into your mouth. This time, I'd like you to take just one raisin and slowly, carefully experience it. As you hold the raisin, notice how it looks. Notice its color . . . its shape . . . notice the wrinkles on its surface. Notice how the light shines on the surface of the raisin as you turn it slightly. Notice the feel of the raisin as it touches your fingers. Notice the roughness of its skin, its stickiness, and its squishiness when you gently squeeze it. Now hold the raisin up to your nose and smell its fragrance. How does it smell? Now hold the raisin to your lips and notice that sensation. What does it feel like as it touches your lips? Now hold the raisin to your tongue. What sensations do you notice now? How does it feel? Does it have a taste? Now take a bite of the raisin. What is that like? What do you notice as you start to chew your raisin? What tastes and sensations do you notice in your mouth? Are there any other thoughts, feelings, or memories that you experience? Notice what you experience as you finish eating the raisin. Now, take another raisin and eat this raisin slowly, making sure to be present to that raisin as you eat it.

Take a few moments to write about your experience. What did you notice about these raisins that you had not experienced before? What did you notice about yourself as you encountered the raisins? Is this different from how you usually experience raisins? Food? Other sensory experiences?

_____

_____

_____

_____

Paying attention to your moment-to-moment sensory experience can be exquisitely nourishing. The raisin, the cup of tea, the lily, the sound of the wind, and the sunlight filtering through your window shades are all occasions to savor the richness of the present moment. You can even enjoy the simple rise and fall of your breathing. Tuning in to your senses gives you a place to rest in the present moment. You might find respite from the voice in your head while taking a hike, amid the beauty of nature, or alone in a warm, relaxing bath. But *any* time can be an opportunity to find comfort in the present moment. Your sensory experience need not be a special event. Simply paying attention to your immediate experience during very ordinary activities can be profoundly refreshing. Washing the dishes, folding laundry, shoveling snow, or standing in line at the grocery store can all be enlivening when you choose to be present.

If you are experiencing anxiety, coming to your senses can help you feel calmer and more grounded. When you slow down your mind, you can savor what's happening right now.

The Observing Self

In the raisin exercise, you took note of the sensations, feelings, and thoughts that came up as you encountered the raisin. Now I want to bring your attention to a more subtle but very important part of your experience: *Who* was doing the noticing? The part of you that noticed your sensations, your thoughts, and your feelings is the core of who you are. It is that part of you that is able to observe and reflect on your experience. It is your Observing Self, the *you* that has always been there, through all the varied experiences of your life. It was there when you were a young child on your first day of school. It was there when you lay down to sleep last night. It returned when you opened your eyes this morning. Your Observing Self is here now. It is the *you* that is aware of reading these words, aware of breathing in and out, and aware of thinking whatever you are thinking right now. Your Observing Self is always there, constant and unchanging, no matter what you may experience in any given moment. When you pay attention to what you are experiencing in the present, you strengthen your connection with your core, your Observing Self.

Strengthening your connection with your Observing Self increases your freedom. It enables you to witness what you are experiencing in any moment without being at the mercy of it. It is what enabled the man involved in a car accident with my wife to respond with compassion rather than anger or fear. When you are strongly connected with your Observing Self, you are able to thoughtfully inhabit the gap between stimulus and response. You can clearly see what is going on within and around you and respond wisely.

Usually your Observing Self resides in the background. While you are busy living your life, it is there, but you may not be explicitly aware of it. That's because in most moments you tend to focus on the content of what you are aware of rather than on the awareness itself. In the following exercise, you will have an opportunity to experience the specific *contents* of your awareness and your awareness *itself*. This will help you become more consciously aware of your Observing Self.

Contacting the Observing Self

1. Begin by becoming aware of your *sensations*. Take a little time to simply notice—without judging or resisting—any physical sensations you can experience. Notice the feeling of your clothes against your skin and the sensation of contact your body has with the surface you are sitting on. Notice the sensations of your breathing.

   Be aware of any sounds that you hear. Soft, loud, singular, or constant, just let the sounds flow right through you. Notice as well what you are seeing. Be aware of the words on the page, the book, and any other objects in the room.

   When you feel you have spent enough time with your physical sensations, move on to the next step.

2. Become aware of your *feelings*. What emotions are you experiencing right now? What are the feelings that you tend to feel most often in your life? Reflect on the positive as well as the negative feelings—joy, anger, sadness, peacefulness, love, resentment, depression, enthusiasm.

   Try not to judge your feelings. View them objectively,

as if you were taking inventory. When you feel ready, shift your attention from your emotions to the next step.

3. Now turn your attention to your *desires.* As you maintain your objective attitude, consider the desires that most motivate you. There are moments in your life when you are deeply immersed in pursuing these desires, but right now simply reflect on them in a spirit of curiosity.

    When you are ready, move on to the next step.

4. Focus your attention now on your *thoughts.* When you become aware of a thought, simply observe it without judging or resisting it. When another thought emerges, watch it until it disappears and a new one appears. If you think you are not having any thoughts, be aware that this is a thought, too. Watch your flow of thoughts as they arise: worries, memories, ideas, questions, judgments, images, fantasies.

    Stay with your thoughts for a few minutes, and then let yourself move on to the next step.

5. Become aware of your Observing Self; the one who has been watching your sensations, feelings, desires, and thoughts. The Observing Self is not an image or a thought. It is the center of awareness that has been observing all these experiences and is distinct from them. Take a couple of minutes to fully appreciate that at your core *you are* the Observing Self, a center of pure awareness.

Developing your connection with the Observing Self is profoundly helpful in becoming free of depression. It enables you to step back from any thought, sensation, emotion, or desire and not be consumed by it. When you strengthen your connection to the Observing Self, you become less likely to get stuck in rumination. You become better able to step back and detach from the negative thinking that fuels depression. When you lift the veil of negative thinking, you can see yourself and your life clearly. And when you see things clearly, you can respond effectively.

The Observing Self is by nature wise and caring, and it can defuse self-critical and pessimistic thinking. It has the ability to act as a wise, loving parent who comforts a hurt child. The awareness of the Observing Self is expansive. It connects you to a deep source of intelligence.

Meditation

One of the most powerful ways to be fully present and awake to life is through meditation. Practicing meditation strengthens your connection to the Observing Self. By nonjudgmentally paying attention to your moment-to-moment experience, you become better at observing your thoughts and feelings without being enmeshed in them. When you free yourself from the brainwashing effect of your ongoing subjective judgments, you can see things as they really are. With clear perception, your mood improves and you become better able to handle the challenges you confront in life.

Please do not be intimidated by the idea of meditation. It is not mysterious or esoteric. In fact, it is extremely simple and practical. I have found that just about everyone can learn to meditate with some instruction and a willingness to practice regularly. I encourage most of my clients to meditate. Those who do, develop greater calmness and clarity, and recover from depression more rapidly.

I recommend beginning with a simple breath-focused meditation. (The belly breathing technique described in Chapter 6 is a good foundation for this practice.) By engaging in slow, full, natural breathing, your body relaxes and your mind tends to become calm and clear. Slow, relaxed breathing helps to balance your nervous system and create an optimal ratio of oxygen to carbon dioxide in your blood. Meditation quiets mental and physical agitation. It also helps to relieve the ongoing stress—and accompanying tension, exhaustion, and hopelessness—that typically comes with depression.

Slow, relaxed breathing activates the parasympathetic nervous system, the part of the autonomic nervous system that balances your body's stress reaction. This breathing technique also stimulates the vagus nerve, a large nerve bundle that connects the digestive organs, the heart, and the brain. Using the breath to activate the vagus nerve, which is so crucial to balancing the stress response, has far-reaching health benefits. Blood pressure and heart rate decrease, digestion is enhanced, and levels of cortisol and blood sugar decrease.

Regularly practicing breath-focused meditation also has profound effects on the brain. The part of the brain associated with anxiety, fear, and unpleasant thoughts (the right prefrontal cortex) calms down. MRIs and PET scans have also shown that meditation activates the part of the brain associated with positive thoughts and good feelings (the left prefrontal cortex). This pattern of brain activation and positive emotion persists outside of meditation, producing long-term mood enhancement.

Experienced practitioners of mindfulness meditation have been found to have more neurons and neuronal connections in the insula, a brain region associated with attention and sensory processing. This makes sense, given that the process of meditation involves consciously focusing one's attention. Strengthening this region of the brain is important for improving concentration, something many depressed people have difficulty maintaining.

Slow, relaxed breathing is an ideal focal point for meditation. Its physiological effects support the cultivation of calm, clear, meditative awareness. It is one of the quickest and simplest ways to shift into a calm state. The visceral experience of paying attention to your breathing helps you feel at home in your body.

As you experience that inner *physical* space, the process of meditation enables you to develop a welcoming sense of inner *psychological* space. In meditation, you compassionately and nonjudgmentally pay attention to your thoughts, feelings, sensations, and desires, without becoming attached to them. When you hold your inner experiences with compassion and acceptance, you gradually transform your relationship to yourself and your life. You become less stressed and better able to appreciate the small moments of joy, wonder, beauty, pain, and confusion that are all part of the flow of life.

Theresa's Story

When Theresa called me, she was desperate. A mother of four, she had faced many trials, but none like this: Her 14-year-old son had just been diagnosed with bipolar disorder. He flew into uncontrollable, violent rages. When he exploded, the rest of the family was held hostage as he overturned furniture and threw household objects. Even though she had raised three older children, Theresa was not equipped to handle Robert. Anxious and exhausted, she needed to take a leave of absence from her job as a high school social studies teacher. She had not been able to sleep more than 4 hours a night for the previous 5 months. She stumbled through each day, tense, hypervigilant, and depleted.

In our first meeting, Theresa shared her overwhelming feelings of isolation. Divorced for 8 years, she was the primary caretaker for Robert and her three older children. She was on the front lines in seeking the right combination of therapy, medication, and special education services to stabilize her son. And she had become battle weary. At school meetings she felt judged and blamed for Robert's emotional difficulties; she felt similarly judged by her parents and friends. She dreaded talking with her parents and avoided family gatherings.

As Theresa shared her story, the tension slowly drained out of her features. Expressing her fear and frustration about her son without being judged gave her a tremendous sense of relief. In our next three meetings, we put together a plan for Theresa's self-care, and for pursuing appropriate treatment for Robert.

Theresa realized she could not help Robert or her other children if she herself continued to be at loose ends. We began with slow, rhythmic breathing as a way to calm her racing, reactive mind. At first it was difficult for her to slow down her rapid breathing, but with a little practice, she was able to find a comfortable rhythm, which gradually increased her calmness and clarity. Connecting with her breath helped to slow down the flood of thoughts that moved through her restless mind.

Once she got used to the breathing practice, I showed Theresa how to meditate. She was able to use slow belly breathing to relieve tension and calm her mind. She chose to add a mantra—*I am*—to her meditation practice. She found that repeating it in meditation helped her to connect deeply with her Observing Self. Theresa began each morning with her meditation practice. It helped her find the calm, strength, and clarity she needed to deal with Robert's emotional turbulence. Any time she felt stressed, she used her breathing practice to calm herself. Silently repeating *I am* anchored her in the awareness that she was more than her momentary emotional reaction. She could compassionately observe her experience from a deeper, wiser place.

In addition to her meditation practice, Theresa began walking and journaling every day, and she made changes to her diet. As she started to feel more balanced and grounded, we focused on finding effective treatment for Robert. We touched on Theresa's goals for her own career—returning to teaching—and agreed she would need to wait until Robert was stabilized before taking that step.

Theresa's distressing situation with her son had overwhelmed her capacity to cope. Finding a clear, calm space within herself helped her to handle the issues she faced. Her morning meditation practice provided a safe haven in which she could identify her thoughts and feelings without becoming consumed by them.

Remembering to focus on her breathing and her mantra during the day reduced her anxiety and replenished her energy.

As you pay attention to your breathing, you give your mind something to focus on. The focus on the breath provides a central point of awareness that helps to stabilize attention. Most forms of meditation involve focusing on one thing. That focal point may be the breath, an image, an attitude, or a mantra—which is a repeated word, phrase, or sound. Inevitably, thoughts, feelings, and sensations will come into awareness. At this point, some people who are new to meditation become frustrated because they think the goal is to empty their minds of all thoughts. Emptying the mind of all its contents is not the goal of meditation; in fact, it's not possible. The mind will continually generate new thoughts, feelings, and sensations. The goal is not to get rid of them, but rather to come into a new relationship with them. The new relationship is one of gently observing your thoughts without being carried away by them. When you relate to your thoughts in this way, they tend to loosen their hold on you. When you stop struggling with your negative thoughts, they diminish in intensity. As you practice, your mind will clear and your body will relax. Little by little, you will become less preoccupied with what has been and what will be. You will begin to accept yourself and the only moment you have: this one.

Here are instructions for practicing breath-focused meditation.

The Practice of Meditation

1. Sit comfortably in a chair or on a couch. You can sit cross-legged or with your feet flat on the floor. Make sure to hold your head and neck upright. It helps if the lights are dimmed and if there are objects around you that help you feel peaceful and comfortable. You can evoke that feeling

with a beautiful painting or photograph, a keepsake that is meaningful to you, or a religious symbol.

2. Close your eyes and focus your attention on your breathing. Follow the inhale and the exhale. Let your breathing be slow, full, and rhythmic. This is not so much about *thinking* about the act of breathing as it is about *experiencing* the sensation of breathing.

3. Notice when your attention is drawn to a thought, sound, sensation, or emotion. Simply allow the experience to be there without resisting it; then gently bring your attention back to the breath.

4. If you find yourself judging any aspect of what you are experiencing—for instance, if you find yourself lost in thought and judge this as "wrong" or "bad"—just notice the judgment as "thought" and bring your attention back to the breath.

5. Stay present. If what you are experiencing is pleasant and you notice any tendency to want to hold on to that experience, just let go of it by returning to the breath. If what you are experiencing is unpleasant and you notice any tendency to push it away, just notice what you are experiencing and return to the breath.

6. Remember, we are not trying to get anywhere when we meditate. We are practicing the art of being here.

It helps to have one place in your home to meditate. You can make it a sacred space, filling it with pictures and objects that are comforting and inspiring to you. But it is possible to meditate anywhere. You can meditate in a hotel room, on a train, in an airplane, or in a library. But please, do not meditate if you are driving a car! If you feel a desire to meditate when you are driving, pull into a secure parking lot or rest stop, turn off your engine, and meditate in the sanctuary of your vehicle.

You can practice for as little as 5 to 10 minutes or as long as 30 minutes or more. In the beginning, you might want to meditate for a shorter period, say 10 minutes, and then gradually increase the length of your meditations. If you prefer, you can meditate twice a day.

If you can, it is helpful to meditate at a regular time each day. Many people find that early in the morning is a good time for meditating. It helps to set a tone for the rest of the day. Another advantage of meditating in the morning is that, much like exercise, practicing meditation first thing in the morning guarantees that it won't get lost in the shuffle of your day. Of course, if you prefer to meditate later in the day or if your schedule requires it, then go with what works best for you.

You can also benefit from engaging in mini-meditations for 1 to 2 minutes many times during the day. This can be a great way to relieve stress and refresh yourself. You can do mini-meditations when you feel tense or anxious, or when you find yourself ruminating. If you are going through an emotionally difficult time, you may choose to do several mini-meditations.

If you find yourself too restless to sit in meditation, get up and take a walk, do a chore, or run an errand. Then come back and try again. Usually you'll feel calmer and more able to sit comfortably.

Reflective Questions

Please respond to the following questions to deepen your understanding of presence, your Observing Self, and the practice of meditation.

1. The following was a time when I felt fully alive and aware of what I was doing or experiencing:

_____

_____

_____

2. Practicing presence helps me to:

_____

_____

_____

3. Being aware of my Observing Self helps me to:

_____

_____

_____

4. I find it's best for me to meditate by focusing on:

_____

_____

_____

5. When I meditate, I am aware of feeling:

_____

_____

_____

6. The best place for me to practice meditation is:

_____

_____

_____

7. I have also practiced meditation in other places, including:

_____

_____

_____

8. When I practice mini-meditations during the day, I find that:

_____

_____

_____

9. Through the practice of meditation, I am developing:

_____

_____

_____

Chapter 8

OVERCOMING AVOIDANCE

When we slow down and allow ourselves to be present, we are able to appreciate and savor the experience of each moment. The call of the robin outside your window, the fragrance of the coffee wafting up from your cup, the smile of the woman who checks out your groceries at the supermarket. These are nourishing experiences that can enliven and sustain you. What's not to like?

It is fairly easy to practice presence when your day begins like a picture-perfect greeting card. It gets harder when life brings disappointment and pain. That's when we prefer to go somewhere else. Anywhere else.

The truth is, most of us instinctively try to avoid pain. If you've ever put off going to the dentist, you know exactly what I mean. Our aversion to pain extends to emotional pain as well. We often go to great lengths to avoid feeling sad, anxious, angry, or lonely. We may overindulge in food, alcohol, drugs, or mindless activities to prevent ourselves from feeling things we don't want to feel.

You can also avoid unpleasant feelings by avoiding situations that evoke them. You might avoid going to a party where you know you will feel self-conscious, or decline to confront a colleague about an issue that makes you feel uncomfortable. You might even avoid going to the doctor to ask about a symptom you've been experiencing for fear of discovering a serious medical problem. The avoidance of uncomfortable feelings can be conscious (as in "I am so upset with my sister I am not going to call her back") or unconscious (as in "I can't believe I forgot to call my sister back").

Unfortunately, avoiding potential discomfort limits your potential for fulfillment, as well. If you don't go to the party for fear of being embarrassed, you may miss out on an opportunity to see your friends or meet new ones. If you don't apply for a promotion for fear of being turned down, you lose the chance for a more satisfying job and career advancement. If you stop dating forever because of the pain of your last breakup, you miss out on the possibility of finding love. Retreating from situations that carry the possibility of emotional pain comes with a cost.

You can also escape unpleasant feelings without resorting to a substance, an activity, or the avoidance of specific situations. You can avoid experiencing your emotions simply by becoming numb to them, which is common among depressed people. You may not even be aware that you have turned off your feelings until you notice that vitality seems to be missing from your life. And in fact, it is. If you shut down your feelings in an attempt to avoid pain, you live in an artificially narrow emotional range that lacks energy and authenticity. If you avoid your feelings long enough, you lose touch with the self-awareness and the wellspring of energy your emotions can provide. A blanket of numbness can settle in, insulating you from your feelings. Like a flower deprived of water, your life gradually withers.

Numbing yourself to your feelings takes a toll on your mood, health, and relationships. For instance, if you continue to suppress anger at your spouse for disrespectful comments he or she has made, your anger will eventually come out in some other way. You may overreact to an innocuous comment and lose your temper, develop a headache every time you are around him or her, or have difficulty sleeping. The energy you put into holding back your anger can drain you of vitality, leaving you tense and fatigued. Your suppressed feelings will also keep you at an emotional distance from your spouse.

So how do you deal with unpleasant emotions such as anger? The healthiest way is to acknowledge the emotion and express it constructively. If you are angry with your spouse, constructively share your feelings and ask to be treated more respectfully. If your mate is receptive, your relationship may even improve. If he or she is not responsive, you can express your feelings in other ways. For instance, you could confide in a trusted friend or write in your journal. You will feel better for having expressed your emotions.

Releasing Yourself from Rumination

A frequent companion of avoidance is rumination. Also known as brooding or overthinking, rumination is one of the most common and debilitating symptoms of depression. When we ruminate, we dwell on our problems. We replay past hurts and we worry about future catastrophes, trying to figure out what we can do about them. Here are some examples of rumination: "How could I have done that? I am so stupid. If only I had kept my mouth shut. . . . I'll never succeed at anything." Negative thoughts like this replay in an endless loop when you are stuck in rumination.

Mentally replaying past mistakes is a natural human response when things go wrong. In fact, reflecting on the consequences of our behavior can be useful. We can understand what went wrong and come up with better ways to handle things in the future. It is wise to learn from experience. Commercial airplanes are equipped with black box flight recorders so that in the event of an accident, investigators can figure out what went wrong. The goal is to learn from past mistakes in order to prevent future accidents. In catastrophic situations, reviewing what went wrong is essential. It can save lives.

However, most of the events we ruminate about are not of the life-and-death variety though they may feel that important. We may find ourselves unable to stop thinking about our work, our health, our finances, our relationships, or our family. For instance, we may be upset with ourselves for making a poor financial decision, or we may be unhappy that a co-worker has not completed a task she agreed to do. We may have strong feelings about these issues, but they are not *black box* life-and-death issues.

When we ruminate, we dwell on events, concerns, or judgments long past the point of diminishing returns. Prolonged rumination rarely yields fresh insights or useful solutions. In fact, it can be worse than a waste of time; it can actually be destructive. Excessive rumination can send our mood spiraling downward. The longer we spin our wheels, the more deeply we become mired in a rut. If the rumination keeps us from taking action, we feel ineffectual at best and paralyzed at worst. The longer we ruminate, the worse we feel about ourselves.

There is a characteristic pattern of brain functioning associated with rumination. It can be observed in the prefrontal cortex, the part of your brain that is just behind your eyes and forehead. The prefrontal cortex is where your sense of self resides. It is involved in regulating emotion, in abstract thinking, and in planning and initiating action. People who ruminate a lot tend to have excessive activity in the right side of the prefrontal cortex. Activity in the right prefrontal cortex is associated with processing painful emotion, protection from harm, and withdrawal behavior. Activity in the left prefrontal cortex, in contrast, is involved in approach behavior and positive emotion. When we take a step toward something we are attracted to, our left prefrontal cortex is active, and the right becomes less active. (These left/right generalizations are true for right-handed people. The reverse holds true for some left-handers.)

The neural connection between approach behavior and positive emotion is a powerful relationship. You can tap into this connection to short-circuit rumination and overcome depression. When you make the choice to stop ruminating and instead engage in constructive activities, you stimulate the brain circuits associated with positive emotion. In other words, when you stop overthinking and start moving into mood-enhancing activities, you feel better.

Identifying Avoidance

All of us have ways of avoiding unpleasant experiences. Take a moment to write down some of the ways that you avoid unpleasant emotions. In the column on the left, write what potential feelings you are avoiding. In the next column, write down how you are avoiding those feelings. Include any substances, activities, or other strategies you are using to avoid feeling. In the next column, write the immediate result of your avoidance. In the last column, write the long-term consequences of your avoidance.

EMOTION	AVOIDANCE STRATEGY	IMMEDIATE RESULT	LONG-TERM CONSEQUENCE

In the following chapters, we will explore ways to work on the issues you have identified in this exercise. You will learn how to access your deeper wisdom to determine how best to handle these issues.

Greg's Story

Greg came to me because he was concerned that his drinking habit was getting out of hand. As I asked him questions about his family, he began to speak about his 3-year-old son. Soon, tears were streaming down Greg's cheeks. He had been holding back this torrent of emotion for 3 years. A bottle of wine every night helped him stay comfortably numb in the face of a reality he understood but could not accept.

Greg's son had a brain tumor. After surgery and several radiation treatments, Greg and his wife brought their son home from the hospital, but his prognosis was guarded. No child with his son's type of tumor had ever lived longer than 16 years. Greg was a man for whom most things in life came easily; this was the hardest struggle of his life. He was having trouble opening his heart to a child he was likely to lose too soon.

Greg tried to be the father he had dreamed of being, but all too often he found himself retreating to the emotional isolation of his bedroom on weekends, watching TV and numbing himself with alcohol. Working long hours all week and zoning out all weekend, Greg was content to let his wife take care of their son.

In order to heal himself and become a better father and husband, Greg needed to stop taking the drug that insulated him from his feelings. He agreed to abstain from alcohol and open himself to an emotional connection with his son. Exercise, breathing, and meditation helped Greg calm his rapid heartbeat, sweating, and restlessness. He began to attend Alcoholics Anonymous meetings, where he shared his feelings and his intention to stay sober.

Greg has now been sober for more than 2 years, and his relationship with his son continues to deepen. He has emotionally accepted the reality of his son's illness and appreciates the preciousness of each day he has with him.

Greg found the strength to face the feelings he had been avoiding.

He reached out to others for support and used several tools to stay sober and handle his intense feelings. Physical exercise helped to relieve stress and lift his mood. Breathing practices helped him cope with cravings for alcohol as well as moments in which he struggled with sadness and anger. Meditation helped him cultivate an inner stability from which he could observe his thoughts and feelings. Through meditation and the practice of presence, he strengthened his connection with his Observing Self. Its calmness and clarity gave him the security to feel the emotions he had been running from. When he stopped running, he could open his heart to his son and open himself to the possibility of genuine healing. The love he felt for his son fortified him and helped him stay sober.

Practicing presence enabled Greg to see his son, and his relationship with him, in a different light. It gave him the clarity, stability, and confidence to face difficult feelings, and it helped him recognize negative thought patterns.

In the next chapter, we will explore constructive ways to transform the negative, judgmental thinking that contributes to depression.

Reflective Questions

Responding to the following questions will help you identify your patterns of avoidance and rumination and begin to develop strategies to overcome them.

1. When I completed the avoidance exercise, I realized I tend to avoid certain activities, such as:

   _____

   _____

   _____.

If I were to participate in those activities, I could benefit in the following ways:

_____

_____

_____

_____

2. I avoid experiencing difficult feelings in the following ways:

_____

_____

_____

3. When I consider facing difficult emotions, I feel:

_____

_____

_____

4. When I examine my ruminating thoughts, I find I ruminate most about the following issues:

_____

_____

_____

5. My plan to decrease the time I spend ruminating includes:

_____

_____

_____

_____

6. In order to develop clarity and calmness when facing difficult circumstances, I plan to try the following (*check all that apply*):

Breathing (type): _____, _____,

_____

Exercise (type): _____, _____,

_____

Healthy eating (foods): _____, _____,

_____, _____

Supportive relationships (names): _____,

_____, _____

Chapter 9

TRANSFORMING JUDGMENT

As we grow up, each of us learns a set of rules and expectations that color our view of ourselves and the world. We learn them primarily from our parents, and also from teachers, coaches, friends, and mentors. These people teach us how to think, feel, and behave. We absorb their teachings and internalize them as rules for living: *Don't be a quitter. Always give 100 percent. Don't lie. Be nice to everyone. Don't cry. Don't be so emotional.* Many of these rules are useful for functioning at home, in school, and at work. We benefit from completing assignments on time, stopping at red lights, and telling the truth. However, our myriad internalized rules create a web of expectations that are impossible to meet all the time.

When we don't meet our own expectations, we often judge ourselves as inadequate. That judging function can become unrealistically negative and take on a life of its own. This is your Critic. Each of us has one. It's the voice in your head that judges you and others harshly. You can recognize your Critic by its familiar running commentary: "I should have done that better. I am so stupid. How could I have done that? I can't stand this. I am so naïve!" And on and on. The Critic generates a continuous stream of thoughts and emotional reactions, often so rapidly that you are scarcely aware of them.

When your Critic shows up, you suffer the harsh, punitive firing squad of the kangaroo court. Self-judgments can emerge so quickly and automatically that you may be flooded with emotion before you realize what has happened. The Critic has become judge, jury, and executioner, and you find yourself shackled by guilt or shame before you have a chance to defend yourself.

Many depressed people have very harsh Critics. They carry heavy burdens of self-criticism that drain their energy and batter their self-esteem. They also tend to have brittle expectations about the way others should behave and how the world should function. Learning to identify and let go of unhealthy judgments is a key step toward freeing yourself from depressive thinking. When you do this, you can look at situations from multiple perspectives and consider several ways of responding. Learning to take alternative perspectives and actions liberates you from the narrow, rigid patterns of thought and action that characterize depression.

So the next time your Critic beats up on you for bouncing a check, deleting an important document, or gaining a few pounds, you can step back and look at the situation from a more compassionate and constructive perspective. In the case of a bounced check, you can acknowledge that you are not happy about the $30 bank fee, but it doesn't mean you are an incompetent, hopeless failure. Rather, it reflects that you are human and fallible, just like everyone else. You can choose to learn from the experience by keeping better track of your checking account balance. With some practice, you will become astute at spotting unhealthy judgments and coming up with alternative interpretations. As you do, you will free yourself from the grip of depressive thinking.

One of the challenges of letting go of judgment is that the judging activity of the mind can be subtle and at times useful. The judging function helps us critically evaluate information and make wise choices. It helps us to choose healthy food to eat, friends to confide in, neighborhoods to live in, and work to engage in. It helps us to stay out of trouble. We cannot dispense with our ability to critically evaluate information and people.

We can also benefit from turning the evaluative eye toward ourselves. Thoughtful, constructive self-evaluation is one of the most effective ways to nourish our potential to become the best we can be. Report cards, performance evaluations, and honest self-inventories can give us opportunities to redirect our energy into developing new skills, accomplishing goals, maximizing our potential, and enjoying life more fully.

Conscious, constructive evaluation is essential. This is called *discernment*. But the harsh judgment of the Critic is harmful. How can you tell the difference between judgment and discernment? Usually the judgment of the Critic brings a feeling of shame or self-recrimination; it shows up as an attack on your worth as a human being, rather than simply an objective evaluation of your behavior. Discernment, on the other hand, brings self-awareness accompanied by compassion and self-acceptance.

Let's look at another example of how you might encounter the judgment of the Critic. You may be having dinner with an old friend who tells you about a conflict she is having with a co-worker. You empathize and offer a suggestion. She frowns and tells you that you don't quite understand. Then she changes the subject. Suddenly, your critic emerges and says, "How could I say something like that? I am such an idiot." In that moment you have become brainwashed by your thoughts, accepting and reacting to them as if they were objective facts. In reality, they were subjective judgments. Judging yourself harshly leads to feelings of shame, guilt, and embarrassment that can drain your energy and contribute to depression.

The solution is to realize when the Critic has hit you with a harsh judgment and step back from it. Try to see it for what it really is—a subjective evaluation, not an objective fact. In the example above, your Critic reacted with "How could I say something like that? I am such an idiot." Try to step back from this judgment and consider alternative interpretations. For example: "I tried my best to understand her problem and offer a helpful suggestion. I can't control her reaction to my suggestion. In fact, she may have changed the subject for reasons that have nothing to do with me. Her reaction does not mean I am an idiot. I feel disappointed that she apparently didn't find my suggestion helpful, but I feel okay about myself."

As you continue to practice presence, you will increase your skill at recognizing judgments when they arise. Later in this chapter we will explore practical ways to deal with negative judgment and develop a new, conscious relationship with the Critic.

The Critic can unleash its judgmental force toward others, as well. "How could she treat me like that? How could he have been so selfish?" The consequences of judging others harshly can contribute to depression, especially if you generalize those judgments to a broad range of people and situations. You may come to believe that most people are small-minded, selfish, or mean-spirited. You may then feel isolated, lonely, and disconnected from others. If your judgments of others lead you to *act* critically toward them, they may react by withdrawing from you or withholding their genuine feelings for fear of being judged or criticized. The net result for you is an experience of isolation that fuels the cycle of depression.

Learning to identify and transform your unrealistic judgments of others can be truly liberating. Once you step back and see your thinking for what it is, the quality of your mood and your life will change dramatically.

Sal's Story

Sal had been paying a high price for his tendency to judge everyone in his life. He came to me at the urging of his physician, who was concerned that Sal's agitated depression and high blood pressure put him at risk of a second heart attack. Sal owned a successful Italian restaurant that he had taken over from his father. His sharp mind and sharp tongue made him a force to be reckoned with. The same perfectionism and critical eye that made him a successful businessman were threatening to destroy his health and his family relationships. He thought he knew what was best for everybody, and he let them know his opinions, whether they liked it or not.

During the previous year, Sal's son had left the family business because he could no longer endure his father's constant criticism. Sal was profoundly hurt and disappointed by his son's departure. He suffered periods of depression and found it difficult to summon up the energy to go to work each day.

In our first meeting, I introduced Sal to the practice of presence. He learned to follow his breath and notice the stream of thoughts flowing through his mind. He enjoyed the feeling of relaxation. He was amused by my suggestion that he could just notice his worries without actually *worrying* about them.

In the following weeks, Sal was able to observe the many judgmental thoughts that arose in his mind. When he could see these thoughts for what they were—just thoughts—he came to realize how his perfectionism was driving him and his family crazy. He saw that his frequent, angry outbursts pushed away the people who cared about him and made it impossible for him to receive the love and respect he craved. Tears welled up in his eyes as he shared his intention to stop criticizing and micromanaging his family.

Sal did his meditation religiously during the 4 months we worked together. He was pleased to find that his blood pressure decreased and to feel a sense of freedom from his tendency to react first and think later.

Sal's moment of truth came late one evening in the restaurant as he was having dinner with his wife and 16-year-old daughter. His daughter's arm brushed against her glass of soda as she reached across the table. The glass tipped over, and the soda flowed toward Sal. "Dad!" his daughter screamed as the liquid and ice cubes approached. Everything seemed to be moving in slow motion as Sal savored the fullness of the moment. He sat, smiling, as the liquid cascaded over the edge of the table into his lap.

Sal welcomed the chilling sensation of the liquid as it spilled into his lap and saturated his pants. His daughter's mouth remained open, frozen in disbelief. Was this the same father who had screamed at her throughout her childhood? Who flew into a rage at the slightest provocation? She started mopping up the soda on the table and gave Sal her napkin to dry his pants. "Dad, I'm so sorry. I'll get you another pair of pants. I'll be right back."

"It's fine, honey. I'm fine. Really." He just kept smiling, aware of feeling cold and wet, and of an overwhelming sense of gratitude for being able to sit with it all.

This was a critical moment of insight for Sal. As he recounted the story, he shared the sense of freedom he felt as a result of not having to react. "All these years I've been yelling and trying to control everyone and everything. Look where it's gotten me. In that moment, I felt like the master of the universe. I could see what was happening like it was in slow motion. It was like 'Bring it on. No matter what's coming, I'll be fine.' And I was."

Sal's practice of presence had become a part of him. He practiced presence in many moments throughout his day. When he got into his car in the morning, he'd take a deep breath and appreciate the moment before he turned the key. His car became his presence sanctuary. Gone were the expletives he used to hurl at other drivers. Now when someone passed him, he would smile and breathe and feel grateful for his new freedom.

Like Sal, as you become skillful at observing your interpretations and realizing they are not necessarily reality, you gain a measure of freedom. When you understand there are several possible ways to interpret an event and several different ways to respond to it, your freedom is multiplied exponentially.

For instance, getting laid off from a job is a fairly stressful event for most people. But of the millions of people who will lose their jobs this year, each will have a different reaction. Some will find it a curse, some a relief; some will be thrown into a crushing depression, and others will use it as an opportunity to regroup, reevaluate, and perhaps redirect their career and their life. Each person's interpretation of the event will exert a powerful impact on his or her mood, energy, actions, and future career success.

Even if you are generally self-aware, there are times when you get so caught up in your thoughts and reactions that you momentarily forget they are your own creations and not necessarily accurate depictions of reality. "This is horrible. He let me down again." "I'm depressed because this month's numbers are worse than we expected." If you are like most people, you forget that you are reacting to your *interpretation* of the event, not necessarily the event itself. By choosing how to interpret the event, you gain greater control over how you react to it.

Learning to be aware of your thoughts and not be ruled by them is a very powerful source of emotional freedom. When you are able to witness and understand how your thoughts create the emotional reality you experience in each moment, you take a giant step toward loosening the grip of depression. When you observe the parade of depressive regrets, self-criticisms, harsh assessments, and imagined future miseries simply for what they are—mental constructions—they no longer have the power to ruin your mood and dominate your thoughts and actions.

Gaining this freedom from unwanted thoughts does not require *eliminating* them. In fact, trying to suppress unwanted thoughts usually doesn't work. For instance, if I told you *not* to think about a flying saucer full of blue-skinned aliens landing in your backyard, you'd probably have a hard time getting that image out of your mind. But you aren't actually worried about aliens barging into your house because you know it's just a thought. In fact, you can just let the idea exist in your imagination. You don't have to suppress it, because you know it's not real.

So, on a personal level, instead of believing a thought such as "I am a failure," you can say to yourself, "I just had the thought 'I am a failure.' I know that my mind creates thoughts like that from time to time, but I know that they aren't true." How you relate to the judgmental thoughts your mind creates will significantly affect your mood.

Tools for Dealing with Judgment

There are a number of tools you can use to help you transform judgment. The following techniques will help you to observe your thoughts and look at things from a different, more constructive perspective.

Practice Presence

Being present allows you to *respond to* your thoughts and feelings rather than *react to* them. When you begin to notice that you are reacting judgmentally, take a moment to breathe slowly into your belly. Become aware of the judgment you have made and the feelings you are experiencing in connection with it. Ask yourself if there is a less judgmental, more compassionate way to view the situation. Take some time to listen for an answer.

Heart Breathing

Take a moment to breathe into your heart. For just a moment, turn your attention away from the judgment and just notice your breathing. Now think about something in your life that you enjoy or appreciate. Let yourself savor that feeling. After about a minute, come back to the original judgment and ask yourself if there is another way you can look at it. Ask yourself what would be the best way to handle the situation, and listen for an answer.

When you breathe into your heart and get in touch with a feeling of appreciation, you tap into your emotional intelligence. You invite the wisdom of the heart to respond to the activity of the mind, widening the net of perception to include both head and heart. This allows you to think and act constructively in ways that nourish hope and enthusiasm.

Disidentify from the Critic

When you realize that the Critic is reacting with harsh judgment, take a step back and acknowledge the Critic's presence. This crucial step lets you set yourself apart from the Critic's judgment. Let the Critic know that you appreciate its positive intention to protect you or make you better. You can even express your gratitude to the Critic with a simple "Thank you for sharing." Then look at the situation from a broader, more compassionate perspective. Ask yourself: "How else can I see this? What would be a wiser, more constructive way to view this situation? What would be the best way for me to handle this?" The goal of disidentifying is not to eliminate the Critic. In fact, you cannot eliminate the Critic. It is a part of you. It developed a long time ago to protect and serve you. The key is to see it for what it is and develop a healthy relationship with it.

What Can I Learn from This?

One of the best ways to defuse judgment is by shifting from blaming to learning. Instead of asking, "Who is to blame for this?" ask, "What can I learn from this?" Blaming yourself or others generally lowers your mood and drains your energy. Learning brings a lighter mood and restores your energy. The simple shift from blaming to learning is tremendously empowering.

Forgiveness

Practicing forgiveness is one of the most powerful ways to transform judgment and overcome depression. In Chapter 10 we will explore several strategies for tapping into the healing potential of forgiveness.

Reflective Questions

Take a few moments to reflect on how you are affected by your judgments of yourself and others. Consider some kinder and more empowering ways of evaluating yourself and others.

1. I recognize my inner Critic when I find myself thinking:

   _____

   _____

   And feeling: _____

   _____

2. I tend to judge myself harshly in the following ways:

   _____

   _____

   _____

3. Three things I can do to free myself from the influence of my judgmental thinking are:

   1. _____

   2. _____

   3. _____

4. I tend to be judgmental toward others when they:

_____

_____

_____

5. When I notice myself judging others harshly, it would be helpful for me to:

_____

_____

_____

6. A familiar negative thought about myself is:

_____

_____

_____

A more compassionate way to view this would be:

_____

_____

_____

7. As I pay attention to the judgments I make and try to transform them, I notice that:

_____

_____

_____

Chapter 10

DEVELOPING FORGIVENESS AND GRATITUDE

There are two ways to look at life. One way is that nothing is a miracle. The other is that everything is a miracle.

ALBERT EINSTEIN

How you view your life has a greater impact on your mood than what actually happens to you. Forgiving those who have harmed you and being grateful for what you have will help to free you from depression.

Forgiveness is not for the fainthearted. When we are wronged, hurt, or betrayed by another, our natural tendency is to harm, avoid, or seek revenge upon the person who hurt us. Failure to forgive is writ large on the pages of history. Indeed, most wars, massacres, and genocides are the product of an agonizing cycle of attack and revenge. While forgiveness is taught in the sacred texts of the world's religions ("To err is human, to forgive, divine"), its opposite ("An eye for an eye, a tooth for a tooth") has more commonly driven human behavior. For most of us, forgiveness needs to be learned.

I should clarify what I mean by forgiveness. By forgiveness I do not mean pardoning, excusing, or condoning. Forgiveness in no way absolves the transgressor of responsibility. Nor does it suggest that the transgression was not hurtful. By forgiveness I do not mean relinquishing your right to legal or financial reparation. You can forgive the same attacker against whom you testified in court. Forgiveness does not necessarily have to involve reconciliation. It is often not in your best interest to reestablish a relationship with the person who has inflicted your pain. By forgiveness I do not mean that you must forget the events that have taken place.

By forgiveness I *do* mean reflecting on what was done to you and how you feel about it. I do mean fully grieving the wound you experienced and making the conscious choice to let go of grudges, resentment, and bitterness. When you make the choice to forgive, you release yourself from the prison of rumination. You free yourself from the physiological stress of replaying the transgression over and over. It also releases you from the role of victim. Forgiveness is empowering.

Nancy's Story

Nancy, an earnest, 36-year-old single mother of a 5-year-old girl, came to see me because she was sliding into depression. Distraught and exhausted, she had endured three traumatic losses within the span of a year and was losing her ability to cope. During the previous year she had lost her job, moved to a new house, and discovered that her husband was suffering from a fast-growing, incurable cancer. She had accompanied and cared for him through a dizzying series of medical interventions. He had passed away 2 months before she came to see me.

Nancy was feeling overwhelmed by the demands of her new job, her long commute, and the responsibilities of being a single mother.

She felt guilty about being irritable with her daughter and held painful unresolved feelings of anger toward her husband. She was having trouble sleeping. Her appetite was poor, and she had lost 10 pounds from her already-lean frame. Over the course of a week, I met with Nancy three times. She confided that during her husband's illness, he had been very critical and unsupportive of her. "How could he be so cruel? I took care of him. I was his nurse, his cook, his chauffeur. . . . I supported him . . . and he treated me like dirt!"

Nancy fought back tears as she spoke about her husband and expressed the feelings she couldn't when he was alive. Her hurt and anger were toxic. "I don't know why I married him. Even before he got sick, he never really appreciated me. Everything he did was about him." Nancy was also angry at herself. "How could I not see it? I can't believe I stayed with him."

"No wonder you've been angry," I said. "You took care of him, and you put your own feelings aside."

"But they're killing me. And I'm being awful to Chelsea. I want to be a better mother."

I asked Nancy to write her husband a letter. I suggested she tell him exactly what she felt about how he had treated her, and exactly what she wanted him to know about her situation now. She came back the next day and read the two-page letter. She began by recounting her disappointment and anger toward him for being insensitive and cruel to her. She told him how much it hurt that he had never really been able to see and appreciate her. Her voice began to tremble. "I loved you . . . and I still do. No matter how much of a jerk you were, I still love you. It was so hard watching you suffer. But I'm glad I took care of you. I'm stronger for it. It's tough right now, but I'm going to be okay. I'm grateful for the house, for my job, and most of all, I'm grateful for Chelsea. I want you to know that no matter what happens, we'll be okay."

Nancy put down the letter and wiped her eyes. "I can let it go now. I'm going to be okay."

As Nancy forgave her husband and herself, she began to take back her life. She released her anger and opened her heart to the gratitude she felt for her daughter and her life. During the rest of our time together, we discussed how she could take better care of herself through healthier eating, exercise, and adequate sleep. She made a game plan to begin practicing belly breathing and meditation during her evening commute by train. Her daily practice replenished her and helped her to be calmer when she returned home to her daughter.

I saw Nancy again 10 months later. She looked more vibrant, and she had regained the weight and stamina she had lost the year before. Her sleep had improved. She was doing well at her new job and felt good about being calmer and more loving toward her daughter. In the past month she had begun dating a man and was feeling cautiously optimistic about the possibility of a new relationship.

When I asked Nancy to write a letter, I didn't know if she was ready to forgive. I only knew that her anger was causing her pain and she wanted to do something about it. The truth is, the only way to liberate yourself from the grip of anger is to forgive. As we discussed in Chapter 7, forgiveness allows you the freedom to consciously inhabit the gap between stimulus and response. By choosing to forgive, you are no longer a slave to your instinctive impulse toward anger or avoidance. Forgiveness opens your heart to the possibility of healing.

While Nancy's ability to let go and forgive happened more rapidly than you may experience, it's important to understand that choosing to forgive is a gift you give yourself. While those you forgive may feel relieved if you express your forgiveness to them, the point of forgiveness is to free yourself. Those who are able to forgive tend to be happier and have higher self-esteem than those who are not. People who can't forgive are much more vulnerable to depression. Smoldering anger burns up energy and prevents it from flowing into positive emotions and vitality. In this way, grudges fuel depression. Buddha said, "If you hold onto a hot coal to throw at a person who wronged you, you are the one who gets burned." It may seem as though holding a grudge punishes the one who hurt you; in reality, *you* are the one being punished.

The following four-stage model of finding forgiveness is based on a model developed by Robert Enright, one of the foremost authorities on forgiveness. If you are holding on to lingering anger or resentment, try putting this process into practice.

1. **Uncover.** First, look at the hurt, feel its impact, and acknowledge what it has done to you and your life.

2. **Decide.** Then, reflect on forgiveness and decide whether you want to forgive the person who hurt you. This is not as simple as it might seem. It may be helpful to write in your journal about why you want to forgive this person and what that forgiveness might entail.

3. **Understand.** Now, do your best to understand the person who hurt you. Specifically, try to comprehend what motivated the person's actions, and what pressures impacted the person's feelings, intentions, and behavior. Try to find an empathic connection, with the intention of finding your shared humanity. This takes time and a willingness to open your heart, even if you are not in contact with the person. This is often the most difficult and most healing aspect of forgiveness.

4. **Deepen.** Finally, try to place the hurt and forgiveness into a larger perspective. You may find redemptive meaning in your experience. Perhaps being hurt has enabled you to feel greater compassion and empathy for others. You may also understand and develop compassion for those who have wounded other people. You may reflect upon your own actions and realize how they have been or could be

hurtful to others. There are many ways you can become wiser for having gone through a painful experience.

Here are some additional practices to help you develop your capacity for forgiveness:

- **Forgive yourself.** Recall a time when you harmed another person, either intentionally or unintentionally. Perhaps you broke someone's trust, or neglected to be there when a friend needed you, or lashed out in anger. Be aware of how you feel about having hurt that person. Do your best to understand why you did what you did. Try to see your actions from the perspective of the Observing Self. How might a wise, compassionate person who knows you very well express forgiveness? Imagine exactly what that person would say to you. How does it feel to be forgiven in this way? Do you look at yourself differently as a result? How would you change as a result of this experience?

- **Have an inner dialogue with the person who hurt you.** Have an imaginary conversation with the one who wronged you. You can use the heart-centered breathing technique to bring awareness to your heart and to the feelings that reside there. This can help to open your heart to emotional healing. Imagine the person who hurt you and let that person know the pain you experienced. Share your feelings about the impact their actions have had on you. Imagine that person responding to you with an open heart. Listen and receive with your open heart, as compassionately and empathetically as you can. Imagine expressing your forgiveness to this person, and the impact it would have on him or her.

- **Write a forgiveness letter.** Writing (and not sending) a letter of forgiveness to someone who has hurt you is a powerful way to let go of anger, resentment, and judgment. You can do this for a recent hurt or to release a grudge you may have been holding on to for many years. When you are ready to do this exercise, think of someone who has harmed you and for whom you continue to feel anger. Reflect on how your feelings about this person and his or her hurtful actions continue to affect you.

If you feel unable to release your anger, or if you continually avoid or wish revenge upon this person, then writing a forgiveness letter can be very liberating. Begin by describing the injury that you experienced. Explain how you were hurt by it and how you continue to be hurt by it. Let the person know how you wish you had been treated, and if the person is still in your life, how you want to be treated in the future. Express your desire to forgive and your understanding of the person's actions. Again, expressing your understanding of the action is *not* the same as excusing it. It is an attempt to comprehend empathetically the feelings and actions of the person who hurt you. If you wish, you can end your letter with a statement of what you learned or how you have grown from the experience.

Gratitude

The subject line of the e-mail read "Thanks. . . ."

Usually I open such e-mails with eager anticipation. This time I hesitated for a moment to think about the young woman who sent the message. I had not seen her since we had stopped working together 2 years earlier, when she moved to another state to attend graduate school. Roberta was a shy, soft-spoken woman who was struggling with a dark, despairing depression when she first came to see me. Having grown up in an abusive family, she suffered from chronically low self-esteem and recurrent suicidal feelings. During the 3 years we worked together, there were many nights I awoke worrying about her. She worked incredibly hard to contain her urges to hurt herself. We focused on ways she could soothe herself, and we worked through the traumatic experiences that were fueling her self-destructive feelings. Gradually, she developed the capacity to handle her painful feelings and began to generate positive feelings. She practiced meditation, took walks each day, and kept a journal. One of the tools Roberta used to help her cope with her feelings of depression, isolation, and hopelessness was to find ways to feel and express gratitude. I suggested that at the end of each day she write in her journal about three things that she appreciated. Of all the strategies she used, feeling and expressing gratitude was most effective for her.

In her e-mail, Roberta shared that she had just earned her degree in social work. She was proud of her accomplishment and expressed gratitude for the support I had given her. She was excited about her new job working with abused and neglected children.

Feeling and expressing gratitude is one of the best ways to improve your mood. By choosing to focus on your blessings, rather than ruminating on your disappointments and shortcomings, you nourish positive feelings about yourself, your life, and others. Practicing gratitude is one of the simplest and most effective strategies for transforming depression.

A growing body of research has demonstrated that grateful people are happier than their less-grateful counterparts. Feeling and expressing gratitude has also been found to help relieve depression. In one experiment, positive psychology pioneer Martin Seligman, PhD, and his colleagues at the University of Pennsylvania delivered online gratitude instructions to 50 severely depressed people. They asked these individuals to write down each day three things that went well and why they thought these events went well. Fifteen days later, 94 percent of the participants reported feeling significantly less depressed. Their scores on a screening tool for depression dropped by 50 percent. This improvement is equivalent to improvements seen when depressed people are treated with medication or psychotherapy, although the latter interventions generally take longer to work. (Individuals in a placebo control group who wrote down three childhood memories each day did not experience an improvement in their depressive symptoms. The mood-enhancing effect comes from experiencing gratitude, not just from recalling random memories.) More important, the effects lasted for a full 6 months.

The researchers repeated the same study several months later with a different group of depressed Web users and obtained substantially the same results. Seligman's team also found that depressed patients participating in a 12-week therapy group (as well as those in individual therapy) who were instructed to keep a gratitude journal experienced a boost in mood.

It is no accident that the individuals in Seligman's study maintained their gains long after completing the online intervention. Gratitude is habit-forming. The number of things you can be grateful for is infinite. As a happiness resource, gratitude is inexhaustible.

There are many ways you can weave gratitude into the fabric of your life.

1. Keep a gratitude journal. At the end of each day, write down three experiences that you feel grateful for. They could be as varied as the buds appearing on the trees in your yard and the kindness extended to you by a stranger. As you chronicle the things you feel grateful for, make a point of not repeating any of the prior entries in your journal and finding new things to be grateful for each day.

2. You can write and deliver a gratitude letter to someone in your life whom you have not properly thanked for something they gave to you. You can deliver it in person,

email it to them, or read it to them over the telephone. Many people experience a sudden and powerful boost in mood after delivering their message of gratitude.

3. Say grace before each meal to express your thanks for the food you are about to eat. If you are eating with others, invite them to say grace with you, and express your gratitude for their presence.

4. Make a point of thanking anyone who serves you in any way—the cashier at the checkout counter, your child for clearing the dinner table, the tech support person who helped you fix your computer.

5. Take a gratitude walk. You can do this anywhere. You can take a walk through your home, taking a moment to consider and appreciate each thing you see. As I walk through my house now, I am grateful for the fire that burns in the woodstove, and the trees and the people who provided the wood to fuel it. I am grateful for the apples, bananas, and oranges that fill the fruit basket and the earth, the rain, and the sun that made them grow, as well as the dozens of people whose contributions made it possible for me to buy them at the market. As I walk outside, I am grateful for the blue sky, the chill in the air, and the beautiful blanket of white snow. . . . I think you get the idea. If you truly walk with gratitude, you will take a giant step on the path toward wellness.

6. Find moments during the course of each day to appreciate the myriad blessings, large and small, that are present in your life. Take a moment now to breathe deeply and think of something in your life that you appreciate. Feel that appreciation filling your heart and extending out beyond your body like a warm glow. By taking time to tap into this experience a few times each day, you can strengthen your ability to generate positive

feelings. Taking 5 to 10 minutes to do this in the morning will help you set a positive tone for the rest of the day.

Reflective Questions

The following questions will help you think about the impact of forgiveness and gratitude on your feelings and relationships. Consider how you have dealt with being hurt in the past, and how forgiveness could help. Consider, too, how an attitude of gratitude could enhance your feelings and your outlook.

1. When I think of someone who has harmed or betrayed me, I feel:

   _____

   _____

   _____

2. When it comes to forgiving or holding grudges, I tend to:

   _____

   _____

   _____

3. One of the most difficult hurts I have experienced is:

   _____

   _____

   _____

4. This hurt has impacted my life in the following ways:

_____

_____

_____

5. I might not want to forgive the person who hurt me because:

_____

_____

_____

6. I might feel better if I do decide to forgive this person because:

_____

_____

_____

_____

7. If I were more compassionate toward myself, I would:

_____

_____

_____

8. If I were more compassionate toward others, I would:

_____

_____

_____

9. Three things I experienced today that I feel grateful for are:

a. _____

b. _____

c. _____

10. A person who helped me in the past whom I have not fully thanked is:

_____

_____

11. I would like to express my appreciation to this person by:

_____

_____

_____

12. By choosing to experience gratitude for the blessings in my life, I notice the following changes in my outlook and feelings:

_____

_____

_____

_____

Chapter 11

THE NEED FOR ACTION

Many depressed people believe they need to feel better before they can take action to change their lives. Actually, the opposite is true; action is a potent antidote to depression. When you do things you value and enjoy, you feel better. If you do those things often enough, you'll forge your way out of depression. If you are tempted to dismiss this idea because it seems too simple, consider the fact that research backs it up: For decades we have known that an approach called *behavioral activation* (in other words, taking action) is a highly effective treatment for depression.

There are several ways in which engaging in activity relieves depression. Pleasant activity breaks up the blocked energy patterns of depression and stimulates mood-boosting reward pathways in the brain. Similarly, constructive action helps counteract feelings of helplessness and hopelessness. You feel empowered knowing you can take action that makes you feel better. Constructive activity gets you out of your head and out of the depressing vortex of rumination. When you stop worrying and start *doing*, you feel better. Once you feel better, you can handle your problems more effectively.

It is especially important to initiate activity in the morning. Many people struggling with depression find mornings to be the most difficult part of the day. Poor sleep, low energy, and a busy mind can make mornings a gnarly time filled with rumination and not much action. The key to overcoming the morning doldrums is to get moving. For some, doing the morning chores sparks them into action. These tasks may be as mundane as emptying the dishwasher, going outside to get the morning newspaper, making the beds, or folding the laundry. For others, it's preparing breakfast and getting the kids up and ready for school. All these routine tasks get your energy flowing. It helps to have a regular, automatic routine that you don't have to think about.

As discussed in Chapter 2, exercise is an especially invigorating way to start the day. Working out in the morning jump-starts your metabolism, brightens your mood, and is the perfect antidote to the morning doldrums. Vigorous physical activity gets your blood circulating, which nourishes your brain with oxygen. Another way to get your energy moving in the morning is to engage in the breath of joy for a few minutes (see page 109). Once you start moving and get your energy flowing, your thinking will become more constructive and optimistic. Ruminative thoughts will tend to drop away, and you'll find it easier to be fully awake to what is happening in the moment. As you engage in your morning activities, you can practice being present. Rather than ruminating, you can appreciate the feeling of the morning air as you walk outside to get your newspaper. The morning is a wonderful time to "come to your senses" and experience the vitality of your present-moment sensory experience.

It is especially helpful to get outside in the morning. I recommend this to many of my depressed patients. Sunlight sends a powerful message to your brain and body to become fully awake. It stimulates the production of serotonin, which provides a feeling of calm and well-being.

Madelaine's Story

The morning was the worst part of Madelaine's day. She awoke surrounded by a dark, dense cloud of ruminative thoughts that made it a struggle for her to get showered, dressed, fed, and out the door in time to make it to work. When her dog barked at 6:30 or 7:00 a.m., she would let him out in the fenced yard and then head back to bed to rest for another 20 minutes. When she finally got out of bed, she felt lethargic and out of sorts.

We brainstormed how she could approach the morning differently. Madelaine came up with the idea of taking her dog for a 20-minute walk rather than crawling back into bed. After a few days of struggling, she found herself looking forward to getting outside and feeling her energy flowing. This small change in her daily routine made a huge change in her morning mood that carried into the rest of her day.

When activity connects you with other people, it is especially effective. We are social creatures, and engaging meaningfully with others (both human and animal) has a way of bringing us to life. And if your social activity provides assistance to others, you'll feel even better for it. When you give of yourself to help others, you receive at least as much of a lift as the person to whom you give.

Most people intuitively know they feel better when they are active. Their challenge, however, is to take that first step of initiating action. Even though they know they'll feel better if they take a walk, it can be difficult to get motivated to get off the couch. Much of my work involves helping people get off the couch and into their lives.

Barbara's Story

Barbara was in the midst of a major depressive episode when she first called me. She'd been struggling with low-grade depression for several years and wasn't improving, despite treatment with several antidepressants.

Barbara was shy and quiet by nature, and her feelings were easily hurt. A few weeks before she came to see me, she'd been insulted by a relative at a family gathering. She was mortified. For weeks afterward, Barbara ruminated about what had happened, replaying her anger and embarrassment. Her chronic low-grade depression deepened. She grew reluctant to leave her home, and she stopped seeing her parents, siblings, and friends. Her physician became worried about her and urged her to call me.

When I first met Barbara, her appearance reflected her mood: There were dark circles under her weary brown eyes, and she seemed to move in slow motion. She said that she felt hopeless. While there were a number of issues we would need to address, I felt that one of the most important things Barbara could do for herself at that point was to become more active. She needed to get out of her house, go for a walk, get fresh air and sunlight, and connect with other people. But she had little energy and even less motivation.

We brainstormed ways for Barbara to get out of her house and engaged in her life. She was at a loss, and none of my ideas sparked her interest. Her younger son, however, provided her with a life-changing opportunity. As it turned out, he was about to leave for college. He was debating whether to give up his paper route or find someone to cover for him while he was away at school. He suggested that Barbara cover the route for him. Initially she was reluctant, but eventually she agreed to take it on. Barbara is a caring, conscientious person; she was willing to handle the responsibility in order to help her son.

At first it was difficult for Barbara to muster up the energy to deliver papers to 67 houses. The only thing that kept her going was her dedication to her son. But after a couple of weeks, she actually began to look forward to dropping off the papers around the neighborhood. Her neighbors depended on her. They greeted her with a smile, and Barbara smiled back. She took pride in her work. She learned where each customer wanted his or her paper placed. She went out in the rain, the snow, and the ice. She grew to love her job, and it transformed her mood. A few months after taking over her son's paper route, she chuckled, "Who would have thought one measly little paper route could change my life?"

Another pivotal moment came for Barbara a few months after her son left for college. She and her husband decided it was a good time to fill their empty nest . . . with a dog. They got an adorable cocker spaniel, Buddy, who did more than fill the empty nest—he filled Barbara's heart. She fell in love with Buddy, and they became inseparable. In addition to keeping up with her daily paper route, she took Buddy out for walks twice a day.

As Barbara's involvement with Buddy and the paper route lifted her spirits, she began to engage in other activities that boosted her mood. She returned to the practices of yoga and meditation that she had learned many years earlier. She started working out at home with an exercise video. She improved the quality of her diet and began a regimen of nutritional supplements. With more energy and a greater ability to focus, she also dusted off her old jewelry-making supplies and began to exercise her creativity. She delighted in creating beautiful necklaces and bracelets and giving them away as gifts to her friends and family.

As Barbara's mood improved, she reconnected with her family and friends. She reexamined the traumatic confrontation with her sister-in-law that had contributed to her depressive spiral and made the choice to forgive her. She let go of the anger and embarrassment and felt secure enough to attend family gatherings again.

By the way, when Barbara's son returned home from college, he got a new job for the summer. Barbara still does the paper route, usually with Buddy at her side. Barbara took charge of her life with small, incremental steps. She tapped in to the power of action to transform her brain activity and relieve her depression.

The brain centers associated with motivation, manual activity, and pleasure are connected by a network of nerves. Kelly Lambert, PhD, a neuroscientist who has extensively studied this network, calls it the effort-driven reward circuit. When we engage in constructive physical activity with our hands, mood-enhancing neurotransmitters are released. Many different types of activity can give us a lift: working in the garden, knitting, painting, building a dollhouse, washing the floor, baking a cake, playing the piano. The possibilities are endless.

Constructive physical activity gets energy flowing, changes brain activity, and boosts mood. It also provides relief from rumination. When you engage in *doing* something, your mind becomes absorbed in the activity. It occupies your attention and provides an alternative to overthinking. Of course, the purpose of activity is more than just to distract yourself from ruminating. The best mood-enhancing activities are ones that are intrinsically enjoyable and meaningful to you. If you love being outside, then planting a garden might be a good choice for you. If you love bird-watching, then a trip to a nature sanctuary could lift your spirits. The more you enjoy the activity, the more effective it will be at enhancing your mood. On the following pages, we will explore several different types of mood-enhancing activities. Choose the ones that you enjoy most and create an activity plan that works for you. Ideally, your plan will include activities that are pleasant, constructive, and practical. You'll want to include some that you enjoy and look forward to participating in, and some that provide other important benefits as well.

Let's begin by identifying what's important to you in each of the following areas of your life: relationships, work, recreation, and health.

Relationships

If Barbra Streisand was right when she sang, "People who need people are the luckiest people in the world," then we're all lucky. The truth is, we do need people. Our relationships are a tremendous source of vitality, stimulation, and fulfillment. Take a few minutes now to consider the significant relationships in your life. Now, put down this book for a moment and think about the people who matter most to you: your family, friends, colleagues. See each person in your mind's eye. Breathe into your heart and feel your connection to each person. This may take several minutes. When you are ready, pick up the book again and answer the following questions.

1. What do you value most in your closest relationships?

    _____

    _____

    _____

    _____

2. Whom do you most enjoy spending time with?

    _____

    _____

    _____

3. How do you like to connect with these people? (For example, meeting for coffee, walking together, talking on the telephone, writing e-mails, etc.)

    _____

    _____

    _____

4. Are there any people you want to have less contact with?

_____

_____

_____

5. Whom can you reach out to for support?

_____

_____

_____

6. What can you do to support the people you are close to?

_____

_____

_____

7. What have you learned in this program that could be helpful to you in your relationships?

_____

_____

_____

8. What are three ways you can have satisfying connections with other people on an ongoing basis? (For example: Meeting a neighbor for coffee on Wednesdays, taking a walk with a friend every morning, attending a book club meeting once a month, etc.)

_____

_____

_____

Work

Work means different things to different people. Whether you work on a tractor or in front of a computer, you are engaging in labor for which you are responsible. You might work for yourself or for a boss, get paid or volunteer, work in an office or at home. You may feel that your work is a pleasure, or torture . . . or both, depending on the day. Consider the following questions about the work you do.

1. What do you value most about your work?

_____

_____

_____

2. What aspects of your work do you most enjoy?

_____

_____

_____

3. What aspect of your work gives you the greatest sense of accomplishment?

_____

_____

_____

4. What personal strengths do you use most in your work?

_____

_____

_____

5. How does your work stimulate your growth and development?

_____

_____

_____

6. What aspects of your work drain your energy and your spirit?

_____

_____

_____

7. How could you make your work less draining?

_____

_____

_____

8. What have you learned in this program that could be helpful to you in your work?

_____

_____

_____

9. What are three things you can do on an ongoing basis to increase the satisfaction you derive from your work? (For example, offering to help co-workers, completing projects on time, or taking pride in your work.)

_____

_____

_____

Recreation (aka Fun)

Fun is an antidepressant, so . . . have more fun!

If only it were that easy. If you're depressed, it can be challenging to have fun. But if you're looking for the cheapest, most reliable antidepressant with the best side effects, it's . . . fun. You may not have much free time, you may not have much energy, and you may feel weighed down with responsibilities. You may have been raised to believe that it's not okay to have fun. Or you may just feel too depressed to have fun. No matter how you feel about fun, trust me: It's good for you. If you have a need to legitimize fun, call it recreation therapy. After all, it is a way of re-creating yourself. When you leave your troubles behind, even for a moment, you feel renewed. Fun is therapeutic.

So, how do you have fun? How could you have more fun? Take a moment to think about the role of recreation in your life.

1. What is your definition of fun?

   _____

   _____

   _____

2. What do you do for fun?

   _____

   _____

   _____

3. If you're not doing much that's fun now, how have you had fun in the past?

   _____

   _____

   _____

4. If you're not having much fun now, what's preventing you from having fun?

   _____

   _____

   _____

5. What could you do to remove the obstacles to having fun?

   _____

   _____

   _____

6. Who are the people in your life with whom you have the most fun?

_____

_____

_____

7. What are three ongoing ways that you can bring fun into your life on a regular basis?
(For example, joining a bowling league, hiking in the park, playing bridge, watching funny movies, or hanging out with friends.)

1. _____

2. _____

3. _____

Health

Health is more than the absence of disease. It is the condition of mind and body that enables you to live a full, vital life. The root of the word *health* is *hale,* which in Old English means *whole.* People have long known that health is what enables us to be whole. Let's explore what you do to keep yourself healthy and whole.

1. What do you most value about your health?

_____

_____

_____

2. What does being healthy feel like to you?

_____

_____

_____

3. What do you do to enhance and preserve your health?

_____

_____

_____

4. What do you do that interferes with your current or future health?

_____

_____

_____

5. What has prevented you from changing the things that interfere with your current or future health?

_____

_____

_____

6. What could you do to remove the obstacles that prevent you from taking care of your health?

_____

_____

_____

7. What have you learned in this program that you could use
   to enhance your health?

   _____

   _____

   _____

8. What are three new steps you can take on an ongoing basis
   to preserve and enhance your health?
   (For example, exercising for 30 minutes four times a week,
   getting a medical checkup, eating more fruits and
   vegetables, or getting 8 hours of sleep a night.)

   1. _____

   2. _____

   3. _____

You can use your answers to the questions above to design your
activity plan. The beautiful thing about an activity plan is that it
does more than just enhance your mood. By deciding what is
important to you, you can direct your energy into creating a full,
vital life. Of course, no matter how well you plan, some activities
will be more satisfying than others. There will always be times
when you are happy and times when you are sad. You can't prevent
that. But you can put your heart into creating the most meaningful
and satisfying life possible.

Chapter 12

THE COURAGE TO CHANGE WHAT YOU CAN

Taking action releases you from depression. When you make the decision to become more active, you take a significant step toward freeing yourself from the paralyzing grip of depression. In a very real way, action returns the energy that has been bound up in depression.

Depression can protect you from painful feelings and situations. But that insulation comes at a cost. Avoiding pain saps your energy and enthusiasm for living. Your depression may have come in response to a painful situation you have felt unable to handle or change, such as an unhappy marriage, an unsatisfying job, or a painful health crisis. The thick, smothering blanket of depression insulates you from the full range of your emotions and the challenge of confronting an uncertain future. The inertia and lethargy of depression prevent you from moving forward, keeping your energy bound up in an uncomfortable but familiar misery. Freeing yourself involves facing your feelings honestly and finding the courage to take action.

This step of the program is subtle and personal. Unlike the tools you've learned so far, there are no specific techniques to guide you. I cannot tell you exactly what to do, but I can offer some methods for exploring your feelings and facing the difficult issues you may be avoiding. At this point in the healing process, it is extremely valuable to have a guide, mentor, companion, or therapist who can listen and provide feedback and support. It is easier to confront our most difficult issues with the support and guidance of a wise, caring person. And it is easier to make important life changes when we know we are not alone.

If you are considering making changes to your life, please think about the timing first. If you are in the throes of a severe, incapacitating depression, now is not the time to be making a life-changing decision. It would be wise to postpone any major decision making until you feel stronger. On the other hand, if you are mildly or moderately depressed, focusing your energy on making an important change may help you feel more empowered. The strategies in this chapter can help you access your inner wisdom to create positive change.

If you want to resolve a difficult personal problem, you first have to address it. You need to explore what is actually going on, sort out your options, and decide on your best course of action. When I work with people, I often take a solution-focused approach to confronting problems. We focus on what is happening in the present and develop practical ways to address the situation. I find it is the fastest and most empowering way to solve problems and overcome depression. This approach helped Catherine face the challenge that led to her depression.

Catherine's Story

Catherine looked down at the stamped envelope containing her letter of resignation. After 30 years as a special education teacher—a job she loved—she could not bring herself to put the letter in the mailbox. Neither could she imagine dragging herself back into the classroom that had become a war zone. The prospect of facing one more day of being hit or pushed by her violent students was more than she could bear. Catherine was stuck. When she called me, she said that she was feeling increasingly overwhelmed by her job, to the point where she struggled to get out of bed in the morning. She needed help to climb out of the rut she was stuck in.

At 52 years old, Catherine had given her entire adult life to teaching children with learning disabilities, attention deficit disorder, hyperactivity, and conduct disorders. Loyal, responsible, and down-to-earth, she was an institution in her school, respected by peers and parents alike. Her current group of students was her smallest class to date, but it was also the most difficult. Catherine was in charge of four students, all of whom acted out violently. When they blew up, objects such as books, desks, and chairs became dangerous projectiles. She had a chronically bad back and was no longer able to restrain students physically without hurting herself. Catherine went to work each day in a state of fear, her nervous system on high alert. By the end of the day, she was completely drained. Shell-shocked, she would make the 5-minute drive home and flop lifelessly onto her couch.

If Catherine tendered her resignation, she would receive an annual pension at 40 percent of her full salary. If she worked another 4 years, she could retire at 80 percent of her full salary. She thought carefully about the long-term financial consequences of leaving her career at this moment.

Catherine felt defeated. She struggled with her drive to be a loyal teacher and her need to protect her body and spirit from being battered. She felt she could no longer risk being injured by her students. We discussed the possibility of meeting with her union representative and letting her principal and superintendent know she had a disability (a chronic back problem) and could not be subjected to violent classroom behavior. Catherine learned that another job that involved teaching learning-disabled children who did not have conduct problems would be available in her district next fall. She felt she would be very comfortable teaching those children.

We worked on how she could advocate for herself to request a less-volatile classroom. I explained that the district was legally mandated to accommodate her disability, and they could not require her to teach children who put her in physical danger. Even so, she was afraid of meeting with her superintendent. I suggested she take a few slow breaths and get in touch with the wise part of herself. She had been practicing yoga and meditation at home and was able to find some calmness and clarity when she focused on her breath. When I asked her to envision the outcome she hoped for, she saw herself with a class of students she felt safe and comfortable with. Then I asked her to see herself taking the necessary steps to achieve that outcome. She took another slow, deep breath. "I'm talking to the superintendent, explaining that my current class is unmanageable. I'm telling him I love teaching, but I can't continue under these conditions. I'm feeling anxious, but I'm not falling apart." She took another slow, deep breath. "I think I can do this."

That week she met with her superintendent. He was accommodating and agreed to reassign her toughest student to another setting. She now had only three students, and she was given two aides to help with them. Her situation became manageable, and her stress level dropped substantially. The following school year, she was assigned to teach the learning-disabled class she had requested. She began to enjoy teaching again. Although her back pain persisted, her depression lifted. She began walking after school each day and continued the breathing, yoga, and meditation practices she had learned the year before.

Catherine was able to take the necessary step to change a traumatic situation and pull herself out of depression. She also utilized self-care practices that helped to relieve stress and replenish her energy. By dealing with the stress she was facing in her day-to-day life, she was able to overcome her depression.

If you are feeling stuck in a situation that is contributing to your depression, it is important to confront it. When you are depressed, however, your thinking may also be stuck in a rut. Depressive rumination tends to be dark and pessimistic, and only digs you deeper into the rut. To get out of that rut, you need to free yourself from depressive thinking and open yourself to fresh possibilities. Persisting in rumination won't work. You need a different way of thinking that offers new insight, perspective, and inspiration.

In the next few pages, I will offer you tools to access your own wise, intuitive thinking. They are powerful techniques for connecting with your inner resources. To use them effectively, you'll need to take a leap of faith, especially if you are not familiar with this type of intuitive work. You'll need to let go of rumination and sincerely open yourself to another source of wisdom. If you are willing to do this, you may find the knowledge and the strength you need to climb out of your rut and move forward.

The following techniques will help you connect with your intuition and inner wisdom. I recommend you try practicing each of them to see which ones are most helpful to you. You may be surprised by what you discover.

Letter from Your Future Self

Take a few minutes to close your eyes, breathe slowly, and quiet your mind. Now, imagine a future time when your problem is already solved. It can be 6 months, a year, or 10 years from now. Let the details become very vivid in your mind. Then open your eyes. From that vantage point in the future, write a letter from your future self to your current self. Describe where you are, what you are doing, and what you have gone through to get to that point. Explain to yourself the essential things you realized in the process. Give yourself some wise and compassionate advice from the future. Once you write your letter, put it aside for a day or two. Then read it as if you were receiving advice from a wise person who knows you well and cares deeply about you. Consider how you can implement the advice you have received.

Inner Dialogue

Another way to access your resourcefulness is to have an imaginary dialogue with a person who embodies the quality you need now. For example, if you feel you need courage to move forward, think of someone (either a public figure or someone you know) who is courageous. Now close your eyes, breathe deeply, and take a few moments to visualize this person sitting in front of you. Ask him or her to guide you through the situation or relationship that is challenging you right now. Ask him or her to tell you what skills or knowledge you already possess that will help you work through this situation. Now open your eyes and write down what you've learned. What did you realize about yourself that could help you to deal with the challenge you are facing?

Drawing on Your Intuitive Wisdom

This process involves creating a series of drawings to help you access your intuitive wisdom. You will need some crayons or colored markers and three sheets of blank paper. You may want to play some relaxing music to support your creative process.

Begin by taking a few minutes to do a short meditation. *Imagine yourself as you are currently.* Let the image of yourself develop. You might be in a realistic situation or one you have never encountered. Just be open to it. You may be by yourself or with other people, indoors or outdoors. Notice the feelings, images, and sensations that come to mind. Be open to any words or sounds that emerge with the image.

Now, open your eyes. On a sheet of paper, draw what you have just experienced. Your drawing can be as large or as small as you like. It can be abstract or realistic. Feel free to use visual symbols or words to more fully express your experience. Don't worry about whether your drawing is a perfect work of art. No one is going to judge it. The purpose is to express what you are experiencing. Once you have completed your picture, put it aside.

Imagine yourself as you would like to be. Sit comfortably and take a few slow, deep breaths. Now imagine yourself as you would like to be. Take a few minutes to let this image fully develop, with all the visual imagery, sounds, feelings, and physical sensations. Be open to any words or symbols that come along with the experience.

Open your eyes and take a few minutes to draw what you experienced on a separate sheet of paper. When you have completed this drawing, set it aside, too. And now . . .

Imagine the process of getting from where you are now to where you want to be. Once again, take a few minutes to sit comfortably and take some slow, deep breaths. Now allow an image to emerge of how you can get from where you are now to where you want to be. That is, picture what needs to happen in order to get from the first drawing to the second. If you notice resistance from the Critic—your judging mind—just observe it without getting caught up in it. Just let the judgment go, and stay with whatever images arise. These images may not make any sense to you at first. Don't worry about that; just let them develop.

Open your eyes, and again draw what you have experienced. Just let the drawing take shape, without judging it or evaluating it as it is emerging. Take a few minutes to finish this final drawing.

Now place these three pictures in front of you and look at them in sequence. As you observe them, consider the following questions and write down your responses.

What do you notice in each picture? What do you feel as you look at it? How does each drawing seem different to you now than it did when you were drawing it?

Now consider the difference between the first two drawings. Are they different in form, color, content, or theme? What do the changes signify about how you are now and who and how you would like to be in the future? What do you think about your vision of who and how you'd like to be?

Now go back to the final drawing.

The first drawing is a representation of the present. The second depicts your possibility and hope for the future. The third drawing is a product of your intuition and your imagination. You may find it surprising, comforting, or jarring. It may reveal ways for you to move beyond where you find yourself stuck now. It may help you access inner resources you had lost touch with.

What do you see in the final drawing? How does it relate to your current situation and your vision of your future self? What course of action does it suggest? These steps might involve a shift in your attitude or in your actions. Do you feel ready to take those steps? If not, why? What can you do now or in the near future to actualize your vision? Take some time to write down your responses to these questions as well as any other thoughts that occur to you.

These drawings may catalyze new insights for you. You might experience a revelation or get in touch with a new sense of yourself or your capabilities. Think of them as representing an ongoing process within you, rather than a static end product. Take a look at these pictures from time to time for inspiration, or put them up on a wall as a reminder. It can be useful to repeat this exercise at some point in the future. Each time your drawings will be different. Over time, you may notice that you are becoming more open to the power of your intuition and imagination. You may also begin to see the progress you are making as you engage in the other aspects of the program.

The Blossoming of the Rose

This exercise also uses imagery to help you connect with your inner wisdom and inspiration.

Sit comfortably, close your eyes, and take a few slow, deep breaths. Now imagine a rosebush—its roots, stem, leaves, and at the top, a tightly closed rosebud. Notice a little bit of pink petal at the tip of the bud, surrounded by green sepals. Take time to visualize the details clearly.

Now imagine the sepals starting to unfold and the rosebud opening, revealing the petals inside—delicate, tender, still closed. Watch the petals themselves slowly begin to open. As you continue visualizing the rose, feel that its rhythm is your rhythm, that as it is opening, you are opening as well. Keep watching the rose as it opens up to the light and the air, as it reveals itself in its full beauty. Smell the fragrance of the rose and absorb it into yourself.

Now gaze into the center of the fully blossomed rose, where its energy is most intense. Let an image emerge there. This image represents something very meaningful, creative, and life affirming that is ready to emerge within you now. Let the image emerge spontaneously, without forcing it. Stay with the image and absorb its quality. Be open to any message that the image has for you, verbal or nonverbal. Simply allow yourself to be receptive to it.

Moving Toward Where You Want to Be

After working through the four exercises above, you may want to use the following exercise to help you become clear about the steps you can take to move forward. Sit comfortably and take a few slow, deep breaths. From a place of inner calm, consider the following questions:

1. What is going on in my life right now?
2. Where do I ultimately want to be?
3. What changes are necessary to move in that direction?
4. What are the first steps I can take to make those changes happen?

After each question, open your eyes and write down the thoughts that come to you. Know that nothing you write is cast in stone. What you write today can certainly change and evolve as you do. This exploration simply provides an opportunity to reflect on your current situation and on the steps you can take to make positive changes in your life.

All of these exercises are designed to help you connect with your intuition. You can use these tools from time to time when you feel the need for fresh insight. These techniques will help you become increasingly open to the inner wisdom and strength that is always available to you.

Reflective Questions

The following questions will help you address a difficult situation in your life. Feel free to use any of the techniques presented in this chapter to help you gain insight and develop action strategies.

1. A challenging situation in my current life is:

_____

_____

_____

2. The effects of this situation are:

_____

_____

_____

3. In response to this situation, I feel:

_____

_____

_____

4. If I could take action to alleviate this situation, my life would be improved in the following ways:

_____

_____

_____

5. The best way for me to deal with this situation is to:

_____

_____

_____

6. At this time in my life, I want to direct more of my energy into:

_____

_____

_____

7. One practical step I could take to direct more of my energy that way is to:

_____

_____

_____

8. Daily events can easily disrupt the changes I am trying to make. I am finding that the practice of _____ is keeping me focused on creating my own happiness.

9. When I did the _____ exercise (Letter from Your Future Self, Inner Dialogue, Drawing on Your Intuitive Wisdom, the Blossoming of the Rose), I discovered:

_____

_____

_____

_____

Chapter 13

MOVING FROM DEPRESSION TO RESILIENCE

The bamboo that bends is stronger than the oak that resists.

JAPANESE PROVERB

One of the few things we can count on in life is its unpredictability. All of us, no matter how lucky we may be, are bound to experience trauma, loss, and adversity. These challenging life events—the loss of a loved one, the end of a marriage, a life-threatening illness, the loss of a job, a child in trouble—are potential turning points in our lives. How we cope with them determines whether we become overwhelmed, depressed, or ill, and whether we emerge from the crisis stronger, with greater confidence and wisdom.

All the tools you have been using to enhance your mood will help you develop *resilience*, the capacity to cope flexibly and effectively with life's challenges. Imagine a sturdy, flexible tree in a windstorm. Buffeted by gale force winds, it bends but doesn't break. Its strong roots keep it firmly anchored to the earth. After the storm, it returns to its prior stature and continues to thrive. That is resilience, and you can cultivate it by employing the strategies you have already learned. Let's look at how the tools provided in this book can help you deal with a crisis. The following coping strategies enable you to be resilient in the face of major life challenges:

1. Allow yourself to feel and accept, rather than avoid, your painful feelings.
2. Let go of excessive judgment and blame, freeing yourself from the toxic grip of guilt and resentment.
3. Confront, rather than avoid, the challenge you are facing.
4. Reach out to others for support.
5. Believe in your ability to cope with whatever challenges life brings.
6. Find meaning in your personal challenge. Learn from it and find ways to channel your energy into constructive action.
7. Feel your connection to something greater than yourself.

In the following pages, I will describe how you can use each of these processes to face life's inevitable challenges.

Accept Your Feelings

Losing something you cherish hurts. Whether it's your job, your home, your marriage, your dream, or a loved one, it is human and healthy to feel pain. In the long run, trying to stifle your emotional response is counterproductive. Suppressing emotions saps your energy and can leave you feeling tense and depressed. Ultimately, denying emotions only delays your ability to heal.

If you lose your livelihood, you will invariably feel fearful about your financial security. If you lose trust in someone who has betrayed you, it is natural to feel anger. And if you lose your dream of a perfectly healthy child, you will feel sadness. Honestly feeling and expressing your emotions will enable you to heal and move forward with your life.

A box of tissues sits on the table next to the chair in my office. Even so, many of the people I speak with struggle to fight back tears or apologize when their tears begin to flow. They feel embarrassed or fear that if they allow themselves to feel their painful emotions, they will never stop. I tell them it's okay. Sometimes I'll offer the wise words a client shared with me years ago about her own emotions: "Better out than in." When you let out the feelings you have been holding in, you feel a sense of relief. The energy that has been bound up in holding back your feelings emerges as emotional vitality. It enlivens you and provides energy you can channel into constructive action.

The key to healing trauma is to allow yourself to feel, acknowledge, and express your emotions with an attitude of acceptance and compassion for yourself. As painful as those feelings may be, they can be handled if you bear them with a sense of loving acceptance. Once you do, you can begin to mobilize your energy and direct it toward what is important to you.

Here are some suggestions for facing your emotions.

1. Give yourself space to feel your feelings when they come. For instance, tell yourself, "I am angry that he betrayed my trust." Putting words to your feelings helps you to feel them and witness them, without becoming lost in them.

2. If you experience intense emotions during your meditations, be compassionate with yourself and allow yourself to feel your feelings without judging them.

3. Share your feelings with someone you trust. Don't isolate yourself. I am not suggesting you express your sadness, anger, or fear to everyone who greets you with "How are

you?" Confide only in those people who have a genuine interest in how you are doing.

4. If you have a relationship with God or a Higher Power, be open to the strength and support this can offer you by way of feeling a connection to something greater than yourself.

5. Write your feelings in a journal. The act of writing helps you identify and give expression to your feelings. This can be liberating. Studies have shown that writing about a traumatic event can help to minimize the chances of getting sick or becoming depressed in response to the event.

6. Engage in therapy. Working with a trained professional can provide the safety, compassion, and objectivity you need to feel your emotions and begin to heal. In the next chapter, I'll share some suggestions for selecting a therapist.

Release Judgment

How could this happen to me? Who is responsible for this? What did I do to deserve this? How could he do this to me?

When we experience a loss, an injury, or a betrayal, we often ask ourselves these questions. How we answer them figures powerfully in whether we bounce back quickly or stay paralyzed in trauma's grip. One of the first ways we answer is by assigning blame: It was the other driver's fault. . . . The doctor misdiagnosed my illness. . . . I brought this on myself. . . .

Often, blaming is an attempt to make someone pay for our pain, even if we are that someone. In a court of law, finding blame may lead to a financial settlement in our favor. In our emotional life, holding on to blame may result in a lingering grudge or guilt that just prolongs our misery.

Judging and assigning blame is a natural reaction to trauma. We try to understand what happened and prevent it from happening again. If we're smart, we learn from our painful experiences. However, our judgments often have strong emotions attached to them that can keep us imprisoned in guilt or resentment for years after the original incident. Resilient people are able to forgive themselves and others for the part they played in the trauma, and move forward with their lives.

Sandra's Story

Sandra's voice trembled as she recounted the story of opening an e-mail on her husband Wayne's computer. She clutched her stomach and gasped for air as she struggled to make sense of the words on the screen. After 19 years of marriage and raising three children together, how could he do this? They had had the perfect marriage, or so it seemed. She printed out the e-mail and confronted her husband with it that evening. Mortified, he immediately admitted to an impulsive sexual encounter with a woman he had met the previous week on a business trip. He expressed deep regret for responding to the woman's overture and contrition for betraying Sandra's trust.

I met with Sandra and Wayne several times over the next 4 months. They both expressed their painful feelings and undertook the difficult work of rebuilding shattered trust. They shared how they had drifted apart as Wayne's travels and Sandra's involvement with the children took each of them in different directions. They committed to doing whatever it would take to get through the crisis. As they redirected their energy into their relationship, they rekindled their intimacy and found a deepening closeness.

I have worked with people who chose to stay with their partner after an act of infidelity and go through the painstaking work of trying to heal their marriage. I have also worked with wounded partners who immediately chose to initiate divorce proceedings. In my experience, the spouses who can forgive their partners and themselves, regardless of whether they choose to stay together or file for divorce, remain the most resilient.

Here are some suggestions for releasing judgment and forgiving someone who has deeply hurt you.

1. Remember that forgiving is not excusing. By choosing to forgive, you are letting go of toxic resentment and judgment, not condoning the actions of the person who hurt you.
2. Remember that forgiveness is a gift you give yourself, not necessarily something you grant the other person.
3. Choosing to forgive does not mean being a doormat. You may decide to forgive someone and take steps to prevent that person from taking advantage of you in the future.
4. Ask yourself whether it is serving you to hold on to judgment. Does staying angry at your spouse (or ex-spouse) really help you in any way? If not, ask yourself whether you can retain what you have learned from the experience without holding on to resentment.
5. Ask yourself what you have learned from the experience. What changes have you made to prevent a recurrence of what took place? What have you learned about yourself that will help you in this and other relationships?
6. Most important, develop the ability to forgive yourself. If you tend to be your own worst critic, learn to cultivate compassion for yourself. Start your day with a loving-kindness meditation in which you generate feelings of kindness toward yourself and others. During the day, if you notice self-criticism seeping in, take a moment to breathe in compassion for yourself. Over time, these practices can help you develop a more loving, accepting relationship with yourself.

Confront the Challenge

When disaster strikes, resilient people have a way of facing it squarely and finding the strength to handle it. They believe in their ability to cope with whatever challenges life puts in their path. Even if they are initially frightened or overwhelmed, they find the courage to engage actively with the challenges they face.

Sally's Story

Throughout her life, Sally had been the kind of person who successfully handled one setback after another. She had coped with raising a handicapped child, the premature loss of her husband, and financial hardship with the unflinching conviction that she could and would prevail. But when she was faced with her own medical crisis, her resilience began to waver. Concerned about his mother's ability to weather this new storm, her son asked me to call Sally in the hospital.

Sally's voice was faint when she answered the phone. "I just can't accept this. It's too much for me." Sally's sense of hopelessness was a serious threat to her recovery. She had fallen and broken a hip 6 days earlier. At 91 years old, Sally desperately needed to connect with the positive mindset that had enabled her to recover from fracturing her other hip 2 years earlier. But now, her characteristically bright spirit was dimmed by the fear of lying awake in agony at night and the long, painful hours of physical therapy she would require.

"I can't do it."

I wondered what I could say to Sally that could help her face her overwhelming challenge. "I don't know how to recover from a broken hip," I offered, "but you do."

"That was 2 years ago," said Sally.

"You're the same person, Sally."

I spoke with Sally several times over the next 3 weeks. She shared her fears about the arduous course of physical therapy she was facing. She spoke with the hospital staff about her pain, and they modified her medication to help her feel more comfortable.

Gradually Sally's spirits brightened. She regained her ability to walk, with a walker, and she returned to her apartment. I saw her 7 months later, and she was the charming, cheerful Sally I had met 10 years earlier. Gripping her walker tightly, she proudly displayed her hard-won ability to walk on her own.

You, too, can develop the resilience to face life's challenges by following these steps:

1. Reflect on other difficult challenges you have faced and identify the abilities you've used before that you can tap into now.
2. Reach out to others and express your feelings. You don't have to go through this alone. Good friends will want to help.
3. Tap into your inner wisdom to find strength and insight you didn't know you had. You can use the exercises in Chapter 12 to connect with your inner knowledge.

Reach Out for Support

One of the greatest challenges to our resilience is a life-threatening illness. As I write these words, I'm looking at a green rubber bracelet I wear on my left wrist that bears the words THINK POSITIVE. My friend George, a minister, gave it to me 18 months ago with the simple request that I think positive thoughts for him. He gave copies of the bracelet to 149 other friends of his. George is battling a rare, life-threatening form of cancer, and he is drawing on every bit of human and spiritual support he can. He has generously given his wise counsel and compassionate support to countless friends, family, and parishioners over the past 4 decades. He knows what resilient people know: that we can get through tough times better when we confide in others and reach out for support.

George has been a student of mind-body medicine for many years. He knows that cancer patients who join a support group live longer than those who don't. Dr. David Spiegel, a professor at the Stanford School of Medicine, found that women in a support group for patients with metastatic breast cancer survived twice as long as others who were not group members. George participates in a support group, and he prays each morning with a prayer partner.

Numerous studies have demonstrated the power of social support to help people through crises and to maintain health. One of the earliest and most fascinating studies was conducted in the early 1960s in a small town in eastern Pennsylvania called Roseto. Dr. Stewart Wolf, a researcher with the University of Oklahoma and a pioneer in the study of mind-body medicine, found that Roseto's residents stayed healthier and lived longer than people in any surrounding town. They had much lower rates of heart disease, alcoholism, drug addiction, and suicide. Wolf and his colleagues were surprised to find that inhabitants of Roseto ate no better, smoked no less, and exercised no more than their neighbors in other towns. The only substantial difference the researchers could detect was in the quality and quantity of the Roseto residents' social connections. Almost all of the town's citizens were descendants of immigrants who came from Roseto Valfortore, Italy, in 1882. They lived in tightly knit communities where most people knew one another and attended the same churches and social clubs. People looked out for one another, and when anyone needed help, the community supported them.

The researchers predicted that if Roseto's social structure ever changed, the longevity of its citizens would be negatively affected. A follow-up study of Roseto 14 years later found that is exactly what happened. Many people had moved out of the densely populated town center and into sprawling neighborhoods. As the town experienced economic growth and its citizens became wealthier, social distance increased, as did rates of heart disease and mortality. The residents of Roseto had become just like any other Americans.

Care and support can lift our mood and brighten our attitude. Science is showing that staying connected to one another is also good for our hearts and immune systems. When we are facing a health crisis, reaching out for support improves our chances for recovery and survival.

While most of us know this intuitively, it is remarkable that some people try to cope with a health crisis on their own. Because of shame or fear of burdening others, they resist asking for support. Some men feel that reaching out for help is a sign of weakness. Women, to their credit, are generally much better at staying connected to others during times of crisis.

Here are some ways to reach out for support.

1. Join a support group. Most hospitals and some community centers and health clinics host these groups. Gathering with others who are struggling with a similar challenge can be a tremendous source of support, connection, and inspiration. People who have gone through what you are facing often welcome the opportunity to provide valuable guidance and support.

2. If you can't find a support group, create one. Go online, talk to friends, and set up a regular meeting (either virtual or in person) with people who are experiencing a similar challenge.

3. Create an e-mail distribution list for your support team and regularly e-mail them updates. Sending out a group e-mail can save you precious time and energy. It helps your friends and family know how you are doing and makes it easier for them to offer their support.

4. Be open to receiving assistance and don't let your pride stand in your way. Good friends want to help. They can cook meals, babysit your kids, or run errands for you.

5. Caregivers need to reach out, too. Long-term caregiving can be tremendously stressful and poses its own health risks. Caregivers need time off for restorative activities and contact with compassionate people they can confide in.

Believe in Your Ability to Cope with Life's Challenges

One of the most crucial aspects of resilience is the belief that you can cope with any challenge you face. This does not mean you will always triumph over the problems you encounter. Nor does it mean you will enjoy dealing with them. What it means is that you will find the willingness to tolerate discomfort and actively confront adversity.

Even if they possess the practical skills to cope with the challenge at hand, people often falter when they don't have the willingness to fully embrace adversity. If they don't believe they can handle it, they won't be able to. Believing (or not believing) in your ability to cope can create a self-fulfilling prophecy. Such is often the case for patients recovering from a stroke. Those who are hopeful and willing to put energy into their rehabilitation regain more function than those who have a negative view of their recovery.

Anita is a shining example of the power of self-belief. Lying in her hospital bed 3 days after suffering a massive stroke, Anita grasped a pen tightly in her left hand as her right arm hung limply at her side and wrote, "I am going to walk again." Frightened and sad, she was still determined to make a recovery. Anita learned from her neurologist that some of her function might come back on its own, but that much of it would depend on her own persistence and hard work during the subsequent months. For the next 6 months, she put her heart into the grueling work of physical, occupational, and speech therapy. Slowly she regained her ability to walk, with a limp; to talk, slowly and with much effort; and to move her right arm. Anita channeled her energy and enthusiasm into her rehabilitation, and saw results. Her positive attitude was vital to her recovery.

Twenty-one years after her stroke, at 81 years old, Anita has problems with walking and balance. She needs to hold on to her husband's arm when she walks. She struggles to pronounce words and can't speak for any length of time without tiring. She can't use her right hand. Nevertheless, she continues to work relentlessly to maintain the abilities she has. She works out on a stationary bike for 60 minutes 5 days a week, attends Bible and history classes, reads voraciously, and plays mah-jongg with friends. She looks forward to each day with enthusiasm. I know this because Anita is my mother.

When confronted with a massive challenge, resilient people are not immune to feelings of anger, sadness, or grief. In fact, they often feel painful feelings quite strongly. But they also believe in their ability to mobilize the energy and motivation needed to handle the challenges they face.

Here are some suggestions for cultivating resilience in the face of adversity.

1. Get moving. Regular physical exercise, especially exercise that you enjoy, boosts your energy, your mood, and your ability to take action. Engaging in a consistent exercise routine affirms your power to take charge of your health and well-being.

2. Seek out and embrace challenges. Challenge yourself to learn new skills, travel to new places, and encounter new experiences. Learn a new language or computer program, start a new project at home or at work, join a new social group. By stepping out of your comfort zone, you will strengthen your capacity to handle what is unfamiliar. Like strengthening a muscle, the more you challenge yourself, the more resilient you will become.

3. Clear the weeds that are choking your optimism. When you notice yourself thinking pessimistic, cynical, or self-critical thoughts, take a moment to step back and reevaluate. See if you can look at the situation from a different perspective—one that is kinder to you and allows for a more constructive way of handling the challenge.

Find Meaning in Response to Crisis

When we face a major life challenge, it is natural to wonder, "Why me?" Resilient people follow that with another question: "What now?" They look within for answers to help put their lives back together. By opening to the possibility of finding meaning in the face of adversity, you can live a richer, more vital life.

Sitting with clients who have endured life-changing illnesses, injuries, and losses, I am moved by how they are able to embrace their experience. A mother who works tirelessly to raise funds for research into a cure for the illness that took her child. A breast cancer survivor who shares her experience and support with other women who have recently been diagnosed. A cancer survivor who tells me he never really lived until he got cancer. His ever-present awareness of his mortality makes each moment of his life precious. I deeply appreciate the vibrant soulfulness he brings to each of our meetings.

In 1991, I met a man named Steven who was having difficulty coping with his son's HIV diagnosis. Six years earlier, Steven had struggled to accept that his son was gay and living with another man. The father's effort to come to terms with his son's sexual identity paled in comparison to what he was now facing. Over the next 3 years, his son's health declined, and he became housebound. Steven was grateful to the volunteers from the AIDS Outreach Center who delivered meals during the final months of his son's life. Their compassion and kindness buoyed his son's spirits. In the year following his son's death, Steven joined the organization as a volunteer, bringing meals to other men with AIDS. He found satisfaction in helping others and giving back to the organization that had given so much to his son.

Here are some suggestions for finding meaning in the midst of adversity.

1. Finding meaning may involve dedicating yourself to a cause you believe in, as Steven did. It may involve a deepening appreciation of the preciousness of life.

2. Meaning may also emerge as a reordering of your priorities. If you experience a trauma or loss, here are some questions to consider.

   - How have your priorities changed as a result of your experience?
   - How do you want to spend your time differently now?
   - How do you want to be with the people you care about?
   - Are there ways you can more fully utilize your strengths and abilities in the service of what is important to you?

3. A powerful way to reflect on how you want to live is to think about what you would do if you knew you had just 1 year to live. This is not as morose as it sounds; it can actually be quite energizing and inspiring. Take time to write down the things you would do, the conversations you would have, and the person you would want to be. Read it over and ask yourself what steps you can take right now that will enable you to live the life you envision more fully. You can draw on the wisdom you have gained to create a vital, meaningful future by sincerely asking yourself, "What now?"

Connect with the Spiritual Dimension

On May 29, 1995, when a tornado hit their little town in western Massachusetts, Rebecca and her infant daughter were at home alone. "It sounded like a freight train rammed into our house," she said. Rebecca clutched her daughter tightly as the wind lifted the roof off her kitchen. When the wind subsided, rain streamed through the gaping hole in the ceiling, and Rebecca was thankful that she and her daughter were alive. "In those next moments when I heard the sirens and then the voices of the emergency workers at our door, I felt like I was connected to those workers and my daughter and the rain and everything by some invisible thread, like some vast invisible web that was holding all of us," she recalled. When Rebecca felt anxious or had trouble sleeping in the weeks that followed, she remembered the feeling of that invisible thread, holding her securely in its vast web and connecting her to others, and she was able to relax a little.

Resilient people know that they are not alone. When faced with an obstacle that feels overwhelming and incomprehensible, resilient people have a way of reaching beyond themselves to connect with something greater. They may call it God or a Higher Power or a vast web of connection, as Rebecca did. This spiritual connection may be the most elusive and hard to define—yet the most powerful and enduring—aspect of resilience.

In the days after September 11, 2001, many people turned to something greater for support. At Canyon Ranch, I met with a group of our guests every evening. In these meetings, people shared their shock, grief, and support for one another. Two of our guests lost colleagues in the World Trade Center. They shared their grief with the other guests, as well as their mixture of guilt and gratitude for being on vacation that day. After sharing their stories, they read a passage from the Bible that provided a sense of comfort for many, regardless of their religious affiliation. Reaching beyond themselves to a larger spiritual context helped them, and all of us, face the enormity of the tragedy.

Spirituality helps us cope with adversity and stay emotionally and physically healthy. People who participate in religious activities stay healthier and report higher levels of well-being than those who don't. However, many people who experience a sense of spirituality without a particular religious affiliation also experience a health benefit. There are many ways that you can connect with the spiritual dimension.

1. Join a prayer or study group at your house of worship.

2. Take time to read spiritual or religious books that are inspiring to you. This can be a wonderful way to enter your day in the morning and to experience peace before you go to sleep at night.

3. Connect with the spiritual in ways that are meaningful to you. This might entail taking a long walk to appreciate the beauty and serenity of nature, gazing at the immensity of a star-filled night sky, feeling love for and connection with your family, spending time with your pet, or simply being present to experience the miracle of life with every breath you take.

4. Create a sacred space in your home where you feel at peace. Place pictures and objects in this area that are meaningful and connect you with your spirituality. Listen to music that inspires you and connects you with the sacred dimension of life.

Reflective Questions

1. Three difficult emotions I have fully allowed myself to feel are:

1. _____

2. _____

3. _____

2. I have shared these feelings with:

_____

_____

3. As a result of sharing these feelings, I:

_____

_____

_____

4. Writing these feelings in my journal has helped me by:
_____; or not helped
me because:

_____

_____

5. I have _____ / have not _____ worked with a trained professional and found it helpful _____ not helpful _____

Why or why not:

_____

_____

_____

6. Three difficult challenges I managed to handle in the past include:

1. _____

2. _____

3. _____

7. I learned I could handle those challenges by:

_____

_____

_____

_____

8. I can enhance my confidence in my ability to handle whatever challenges life brings in the following ways:

_____

_____

_____

_____

Chapter 14

A NOTE ON PSYCHOTHERAPY

In addition to using the program in this book, you may benefit from psychotherapy. Working closely with a professionally trained therapist can provide you with invaluable support. A professional can give you objective feedback and expert guidance that is rarely available from a friend or family member. Several types of therapy have been shown to be helpful in relieving depression.

Cognitive-behavioral therapy is a good choice for many people who suffer from depression. This type of therapy involves observing your thoughts and replacing irrational or negative thoughts with more rational, constructive ways of thinking. Changing negative thought patterns will help to boost your mood. Cognitive-behavioral therapy also involves changing your behavior through identifying actions that will enhance your mood.

Interpersonal therapy has also been demonstrated to be an effective treatment for depression. This type of therapy involves examining issues that exist in your relationships with others. Through discussion with your therapist, you address and solve problems you're having in these relationships. As your relationships improve, your mood brightens. By learning better ways to handle your relationships, you become better able to maintain a positive mood and outlook.

Mindfulness-based approaches to psychotherapy, including Acceptance and Commitment Therapy and Mindfulness-Based Cognitive Therapy, have both been shown to be helpful for depression. Mindfulness uses meditative practices to help you consciously, intentionally, and nonjudgmentally experience and observe your thoughts and feelings. In the process, you become better able to witness your thoughts and feelings without becoming consumed by them. The freedom from the depressive pull of negative thoughts helps to lift your mood and keep you free of depression.

When depression is complicated by post-traumatic stress, specialized techniques may be helpful in working through the trauma. Techniques such as hypnotherapy and Eye Movement Desensitization and Reprocessing (EMDR) allow the individual to relive painful feelings and memories in a safe environment. With the help of the therapist, the individual is able to process the emotions and sensations that were previously too overwhelming or frightening to confront.

Finding the Right Therapist

If you have never worked with a therapist before, you may not know how to find one. If possible, it is best to see someone who is a licensed practitioner. Licensed therapists tend to be in one of the following disciplines: clinical social worker, licensed mental health counselor, psychologist, or psychiatrist. Generally, it is helpful to receive a referral to a specific therapist. You can ask your primary care physician, nurse, clergyperson, or any other health care provider for a referral. Friends or family members who are familiar with therapists in the area may also be able to give you a recommendation. If you have health insurance, your insurer probably maintains a list of participating providers in your area. Show the list to your doctor, to another one of your health care providers, or to a knowledgeable friend or family member and ask if they would recommend any of the practitioners on the list.

Choosing the right therapist is an extremely important decision. Your therapist should have the skills, wisdom, and empathy to guide you through a life-changing transformation. It is crucial to select a therapist who possesses these qualities and with whom you feel comfortable. Therapy is an extraordinarily intimate and powerful relationship. To be successful, the chemistry between you and your therapist needs to be right. Here are some guidelines to consider.

First, you should feel accepted by your therapist. Whether you prefer someone who is softer and more compassionate or one who is a bit tougher and more challenging, you should always feel completely accepted and not judged for your perceived flaws or shortcomings.

You should also look for someone who you feel understands you. You want to work with someone who is wise and empathic, someone who is genuinely capable of appreciating the challenges you are facing and the feelings you are having in response to them.

You want to choose someone who is willing to tell you at the beginning of therapy how they tend to work with clients. It is important to consider whether the therapist's approach feels comfortable and reasonable to you.

Some therapists tend to be more vocal and active with their clients, and some are more reserved. It is important to get a sense of what level of interaction you feel most comfortable with from your therapist.

There are a number of signs to look for early on that will help you determine if a therapist is *not* the right match for you. For example, if he or she does not seem to be genuinely interested in you or is critical of your thoughts or actions, this is not the right person for you. If the therapist seems preoccupied or inattentive, or if he or she forgets important details you have shared in a previous session, this person will probably not be helpful to you. You are also unlikely to benefit fully if the therapist is not knowledgeable about a condition you struggle with, such as an eating disorder, depression, or a phobia, or specific concerns you want to address, such as marital or parenting issues.

Choosing to end a therapeutic relationship that's not working can be a daunting prospect. It may be difficult to know whether your lack of progress is a result of a poor fit between you and your therapist or simply because you are stuck. If possible, discuss your lack of progress with your therapist. Sometimes you and your therapist can identify what's not working and address it in a way that enables you to progress. If that doesn't happen and you become convinced that your therapist is not the right person for you, it is best to let your therapist know. Don't worry about hurting your therapist's feelings. The time and energy you put into therapy is one of the most important investments you will ever make. If your initial attempt is not productive, make a change and find a therapist with whom you can work effectively.

Finding an Affordable Therapist

Unfortunately, one of the biggest challenges to engaging in therapy is affordability. Therapy can be quite expensive. If you have health insurance, explore the options your policy offers. Most insurance providers offer some reimbursement for psychotherapy. Call your carrier and find out exactly how much coverage you have for psychotherapy and which providers are covered. You will want to know this before you begin to contact potential providers, and you will want to find a therapist who will accept the payment allowed by your insurance carrier. Also, consider whether you can afford the deductible and co-payments you will be required to pay over a period of time.

Some therapists maintain a sliding fee scale or reserve a few slots in their practice for clients who are unable to pay their full fee. If you can't afford the full fee, do not be embarrassed to ask if a therapist would be willing to work with you at a reduced fee. If their practice is full, they may be able to refer you to colleagues who also accept reduced fees. Most cities also have low-cost clinics. You can find out about these clinics through your physician, social workers, the internet, or your local phone book. Many local hospitals, clinics, and graduate schools also offer low-cost therapy with psychology interns, psychiatric residents, and students of social work, nursing, and counseling. Although trainees have less experience than more-seasoned professionals, many are often deeply committed, compassionate, and quite skillful. They also receive supervision from senior clinicians to provide guidance when they need it.

Chapter 15

●CREATING YOUR ACTION PLAN

A goal without a plan is just a wish.

ANTOINE DE SAINT-EXUPERY

Many people find it helpful to start this program by creating a written action plan. It helps them get organized, focused, and committed. However, not everyone wants or needs to develop a written plan. I leave that decision to you. In the following pages, you will find instructions and forms to guide you through the process of writing a detailed action plan.

You can think of your plan as a blueprint. If you were building a house, your blueprint would show you how all the building materials fit together. It would be precise and easy to follow. By referring to it, you would create a structure that is strong, sustainable, and comfortable to live in.

Your plan should include all the resources you will need as well as an approximate schedule. Keeping a journal with the elements of your plan and your ongoing responses will help clarify your thoughts and feelings. You may want to go back to the reflective questions at the end of each chapter to find ideas you can incorporate into your plan.

I suggest you begin your action plan in the order presented below. In the first few weeks, focus on the physical components of the program. They are the most tangible and often provide a rapid boost in energy that you can tap into as you engage in the second half of the program.

Nutrition

If you are going to change your diet, you'll want to create a sample menu, plan your meals, and make a list of the foods you will be buying. Use the sample meal plans beginning on page 212 to get you started.Consult the list of supplements on page 294. During the first week, buy those supplements that will be part of your nutritional plan.

Exercise

Design your exercise plan and write it down. The form on page 198 can help you track your exercise activity. Think about any additional resources you will need to implement your exercise plan. Would it help to join a gym? Would you benefit from working with a personal trainer? Do you need to buy exercise gear, such as walking shoes? Do you want to ask one or more friends to exercise with you? When do you plan to exercise? Writing your exercise sessions into your weekly schedule affirms your commitment and helps you stay focused.

Sleep

Include details of your sleep routine or sleep aids. You can include your bedtime and wake-up time, as well as ways to relax and wind down before sleep.

Light

Determine whether you need to increase your exposure to bright light. If you live in a sunny climate year round and spend a lot of time outdoors, it may not be necessary. If you don't get much exposure to sunlight, think about how you can get the bright light you need. If you plan to spend more time outdoors, include when and where you plan to do this. If you will be using an indoor light box, indicate the specific fixture you intend to purchase and how you plan to use it.

Breathing

Think about the breathing techniques you learned in Chapter 6. Which ones do you plan to use regularly? It can be helpful to have a consistent time each day to practice your breathing and meditation. Many people find that practicing breathing and meditation in the morning is a relaxing and energizing way to start the day. Alternatively, you may find that planned "breathing breaks" throughout the day are refreshing and restorative.

Presence

Write down some of the ways you plan to practice presence. If you will be practicing meditation, include when and where you plan to practice. If you will be getting additional resources, such as a meditation timer or a cushion, include that here, too.

Transforming Judgment

In this section you can record your intention to transform judgment. For instance, you could write: "Be kinder to myself about being a good parent," "Be more compassionate toward my husband," or "Be more understanding of my fellow employees."

Forgiveness

Think for a moment about how you can practice forgiveness. Is there someone in your life you're ready to forgive? If so, consider using one of the strategies discussed in Chapter 10.

Gratitude

Reflect on how you can cultivate an attitude of gratitude in your life. You can designate a section of your journal for writing about things you feel grateful for. You may want to set some time aside each day to write about what you feel grateful for. You may choose to say grace before meals, or begin meetings by expressing appreciation to others who are present.

Action

What are the mood-enhancing activities and habits you want to build into your life? Take a few minutes to review your answers to the questions in Chapter 11. What are the steps you identified in the areas of relationships, work, fun, and health? Jot down in your journal the important actions you intend to take in each area.

Your Support Person

Share your plan with your support person. Let that person know what he or she can do to be helpful to you. Would you like to be asked how you are doing with certain aspects of your plan? Would you like your support person to give you feedback or observations? Would you like acknowledgment and encouragement? Don't be bashful about letting your needs be known. If you are working with a therapist, discuss your plan with him or her. If your therapist does not understand the elements of your plan, consider sharing this book.

Monitor Your Progress

You may find it helpful to reflect on your experience at the end of each day. By reviewing what you did and how you felt, you will gain insight that may help you maintain your progress. You will find a daily check-in form on page 242 for recording your observations. Feel free to make copies. You can keep your completed check-in forms in a notebook to monitor your progress. Once a week, take a few minutes to review the entries for the previous 7 days. Do you spot any patterns? Do you see ways to positively modify your approach? Every other week, fill out the CES-D assessment in the introduction of this book and see how you are doing. The effects of your lifestyle changes will work synergistically, building a strong foundation of energy and positive mood. Most people feel significantly better after 6 weeks.

The forms on the following pages can be used to help you create your action plan. You may find it helpful to photocopy these pages and put them in a notebook with copies of the daily check-in form as well as blank pages to record your observations as you progress through the program.

Nutrition

My nutrition plan involves eating more of the following foods:

_____

_____

My nutrition plan involves eating less of the following foods:

_____

_____

I will take the following nutritional supplements each day:

_____

_____

A typical day's meals will look something like this:

Breakfast:

_____

_____

Snack:

_____

Lunch:

_____

_____

Snack:

_____

Dinner:

_____

_____

I will make use of the following resources to stay on track
(books, stores, restaurants, support people, Web sites):

_____

_____

Exercise

My weekly exercise plan includes:

ACTIVITY	WHEN	DURATION	WHERE	WITH WHOM

I will purchase the following exercise gear:

_____

I will receive exercise guidance, support, or companionship
from:

_____

If my motivation to exercise drops, I will confront it by:

_____

_____

Sleep

Planned bedtime: _____

Planned wake-up time: _____

Evening bedtime routine: _____

_____

Nutritional supplements to support sleep: _____

_____

Lifestyle practices to support healthy sleep: _____

_____

Strategies for getting back to sleep during the night, if needed:

_____

_____

Potential obstacles to sound sleep: _____

_____

Strategies to overcome obstacles: _____

_____

Light

I plan to get outdoor exposure to sunlight:

WHERE	WHEN	HOW LONG

I plan to get indoor exposure to high-intensity light:

WHERE	WHEN	HOW LONG

I plan to purchase this light fixture:

_____

Breathing

Relaxing breathing practices I plan to use:

BREATHING PRACTICE	WHEN

Energizing breathing practices I plan to use:

BREATHING PRACTICE	WHEN

Presence

I plan to practice presence in the following ways:

_____

_____

_____

I plan to practice meditation:

WHEN	WHERE	HOW LONG

Transforming Judgment

I'll try to be kinder to myself in the following ways: _____

_____

I'll try to be less judgmental toward others in the following
ways: _____

_____

Forgiveness

I plan to be more forgiving toward the following people:

_____

_____

I intend to forgive myself for:

_____

_____

Gratitude

I plan to welcome the experience of gratitude in the following ways:

_____

_____

_____

I plan to express gratitude to others in the following ways:

_____

_____

_____

Action

I plan to engage in the following specific actions:

Relationships

1. _____

_____

2. _____

_____

3. _____

_____

Work

1. _____

   _____

2. _____

   _____

3. _____

   _____

Fun

1. _____

   _____

2. _____

   _____

3. _____

   _____

Health

1. _____

   _____

2. _____

   _____

3. _____

PART III

WORKING WITH THE
PROGRAM

Chapter 16

MOOD-BOOSTING MENUS AND RECIPES

My 2-week meal plan and recipes provide you with the nutrients you'll need to maintain a stable mood, high energy, and good focus throughout the day, and to settle into a restorative night's sleep. My plan includes nutritious ingredients that will enhance your well-being. Additionally, the following menu:

- **Ensures you get plenty to eat.** Each day, you'll be eating three meals and two snacks.
- **Pumps up the protein.** Animal or plant proteins are included in every meal and snack to help stabilize blood sugar and prevent mood or cognitive changes linked to low blood sugar.
- **Keeps you full of fruits and veggies.** You'll eat at least five servings of vegetables and fruits each day, including lots of leafy greens and beans that provide folate, an important precursor for neurotransmitters. Low folate has been strongly linked to depression.

- **Features berries and curry.** Both are proven brain protectors.
- **Emphasizes good fats.** Omega-3 fatty acids, important for proper brain function and mood stabilization, are particularly emphasized. Fish and seafood are included several times a week, along with omega-3 enhanced foods such as eggs, mayonnaise, and butter substitute spread. Healthy-fat foods such as walnuts, almonds, avocadoes, olives, sunflower seeds, and olive oil are featured as well.
- **Eliminates bad fats.** Eliminating trans fats and keeping saturated fats and polyunsaturated fats such as corn oil to a minimum is key to supporting mind-body health.
- **Includes whole grains.** Brown rice, oatmeal, and whole grain breads, and crackers offer delicious alternatives to refined grains.
- **Skips the sugar.** High-fructose corn syrup, refined sugar, and artificial sweeteners are avoided. Many people see dramatic results just by giving up sugar.
- **Steers clear of artificial ingredients.** MSG, artificial sweeteners, and foods exposed to herbicides, pesticides, hormones, and added antibiotics are not included.
- **Avoids alcohol and caffeine.** These can interfere with the relaxing effects of serotonin and, in the long run, sap energy.

The meals and snacks in this chapter are easy to prepare and can often be made ahead of time. You'll find variations on some recipes, showing you how easy it is to make changes. My intention is to make healthy eating simple, creative, and pleasurable, so flexibility is built into the plan. If you feel rushed after work and don't want to spend much time cooking dinner, there are ways to keep weeknights stress free. Spend some time over the weekend preparing. Chopping vegetables, mixing up sauces, or fully cooking a dish to refrigerate or freeze for weeknights helps you stay on a healthy course. The quickest meal of the week is planned for Day 5

(Friday, or the last day of your workweek) and longer-cooking meals are planned on Days 6 and 7 (Saturday and Sunday, or whatever days you have off). If you feel there are more new recipes to prepare than you can handle, replace them with a big salad with grilled chicken or fish on a few nights!

To avoid toxins that can cause cancer, damage the nervous system and neurotransmitter production, or interfere with the action and production of hormones, I recommend buying local, organically grown produce whenever possible. If you can't switch completely to organic, try to choose organic varieties of the "dirty dozen": those fruits and vegetables most tainted with pesticide residues. They are listed below, from highest to lowest pesticides levels. (Numbers 2 and 3 are actually tied)

1. strawberries
2. bell peppers (green and red)
3. spinach
4. cherries
5. peaches
6. cantaloupe
7. celery
8. apples
9. apricots
10. green beans
11. grapes
12. cucumbers

Nonorganic fruits and vegetables should be washed with a mild detergent or peeled to help reduce pesticide levels.

I recommend that you use grass-fed and, if possible, grass-*finished* beef, both free of antibiotics and hormones. There has been some abuse of labeling of these products. For instance, the word *natural* can be misleading. The Cornucopia Institute, an organic foods watchdog group (cornucopia.org) reports on the abuse of natural food labeling. Your best bet when shopping in supermarkets is to buy only those meat and dairy products that have the green and white USDA Organic label. It guarantees that all animals used in the production of these products:

- Never received antibiotics
- Never received growth-promoting hormones
- Were fed only certified organic grains and grasses
- Had unrestricted outdoor access
- Received humane treatment

Please note that USDA Organic certification doesn't necessarily mean that the animal was grass-finished. You'll have to look for that information separately. Even some grass-fed animals are fed grain, especially corn, for the last few weeks or months of their short lives, and that adds a lot of polyunsaturated fats to the meat. Some small local producers do a good job of producing close-to-organic meat, even if they do not have a USDA certification. Ask for suggestions at a local health food store or check the Web site localharvest.org to find those in your area.

Good local producers often have excellent Web sites with very detailed information on how they operate their ranches and how their cattle are raised, allowing you to make an informed decision. Ranches that deliver organic grass-finished beef include: Alderspring Ranch (alderspring.com), Betsy Ross's Grass-Fed Beef (rossfarm.com), and Hardwick Beef (hardwickbeef.com).

Organic poultry, pork, and lamb come from animals that are not given antibiotics and hormones, may be free-range, and are fed only organically grown feed. These products can also receive a USDA Organic label. Brands include Blackwing (blackwing.com), Wise Organic Pastures (organic and kosher, wiseorganicpastures.com), Petaluma Poultry (petalumapoultry.com), and Organic Prairie (organicprairie.com).

Even fish can be a problem. Farm-raised fish are usually fed antibiotics and grain pellets, and they contain lower levels of omega-3 fatty acids, so I recommend selecting wild-caught fish whenever possible. Avoid fish with high mercury levels, such as king mackerel, orange roughy, shark, swordfish and ahi tuna. Fish can also contain other toxins, such as PCBs, dioxins, and dieldrin. Sardines are an especially good source of omega-3s and are low in toxins because they are low on the food chain. Also, chunk light tuna is lower in mercury than albacore or solid white tuna. For more information about safe fish to buy, go to the Natural Resources Defense Council Web site (nrdc.org/health/effects/mercury/index. asp). There, you can print out a wallet card to refer to when you're buying fish.

Reach for organic dairy products, too, including milk, cream, yogurt, cheese, butter, ice cream, and sour cream. There are more organic dairy products now than ever before, by both local and national producers. Good brands include Stonyfield Farm (stony-field.com), Organic Valley (organicvalley.coop), Horizon (horizondairy.com), and Next Generation, as well as others. Most of these products are available at local supermarkets.

Purchase omega-3 fortified foods such as eggs, milk, oils, mayonnaise and peanut butter. These foods help shift the ratio of fats in your diet toward a more brain-friendly balance by replacing other, less healthy, fats. Still, these products are often high in total fat, so don't overdo them. One popular brand of fortified products is Smart Balance (smartbalance.com). Also try omega-3 fortified orange juice and cereal.

Changing the way you eat is important if you want to increase your energy and improve your emotions, motivation, and outlook on life. Be patient with the process. If you can only make some of these changes each week, celebrate the changes that you've made and know that you'll continue to improve your eating habits a little bit each day. The meal plan helps make this easy for you, giving guidelines for great meals to improve your mood. If the plan works well for you, continue to use it. Or, stick with the recipes you enjoy and replace others with your favorite meals prepared with the healthiest ingredients. Most of all, enjoy your food and your newfound health.

Five Ways to Make It Easier

It is easier to eat well if you do some food planning and preparation. It's more difficult if you always eat out or rely on processed or prepared foods. If making your own meals seems overwhelming, here are a few ways to get organized. Keep in mind that making meals does get easier, over time. Many people find cooking a creative, contemplative way to nurture themselves!

1. **MAKE LISTS.** Plan meals and snacks at least a couple of days, and up to a week, in advance. Make a shopping list and buy what you need all at once. If you buy mostly the same items week after week, keep a typed list that you can print out and just circle the items you need.

2. **COOK AHEAD.** When preparing a recipe, make a double batch and freeze or refrigerate it for later.

3. **STOCK UP.** Keep your refrigerator stocked with baby carrots, yogurt, olive oil, mayonnaise, Parmesan cheese, lemon and lime juices, and hardy greens, such as kale. Keep the pantry full of cans of beans and tomatoes, sardines and tuna, almond and peanut butters, salsa, tomato sauce, soy sauce, and organic broths and soups. Stock the freezer with berries, mixed vegetables, whole wheat pita bread and tortillas, shrimp, salmon fillets and burgers, veggie burgers, and organic meats. Having these foods on hand allows last-minute meal decisions to be healthy ones.

4. **BE FLEXIBLE.** Leftovers and substitutions are fine. If you don't have a particular ingredient, come up with a creative alternative. Think of cooking as a grand experiment.

5. **START WITH SOUPS AND SALADS.** These dishes are relatively fast and simple, and they make it easy to eat more vegetables. Make meal-sized salads using greens, leftover veggies, and meat. Make fun, interesting fruit salads; add lime or orange juice to keep it fresh. Change up the flavors with a touch of lime zest, grated fresh ginger, mint, chopped nuts, or maple syrup.

How to Choose Breads, Cereals, and Crackers

Look for brands that have no trans fats or high-fructose corn syrup, and stick with those that have less than 1 gram of saturated fat and no more than 8 grams of sugar per serving. Aim for at least 3 grams of fiber per serving. Choose real whole grain products—those with whole wheat or whole grain listed in the ingredients. "Wheat flour" and "bromated flour" are white flour, not whole wheat flour. Some grain products are also good protein sources, so always check to see how much protein is in a product. Products fortified with soy or whey protein can have from 9 to almost 30 grams of protein per serving—that's as much as an egg or a few ounces of meat!

WEEK 1, DAY 1

Breakfast
  One-Bowl Power Breakfast (page 221)

Snack
  1 hard-cooked omega-3 egg, sliced
  1 teaspoon Fabulous French Dressing (page 254)
  6 whole grain crackers

Lunch
  Lentil Soup with Turkey Sausage (page 225)
  1 cup salad greens with ½ tomato and 1 grated carrot
  1 tablespoon Simple Vinaigrette (page 255)

Snack

1 ounce Cheddar cheese

1 medium apple

Dinner

Flounder with Lemon Broccoli and Bulgur (page 234)

WEEK 1, DAY 2

Breakfast

1 cup plain yogurt with Berry Fruit Salad (page 251)

1 slice toasted whole grain bread with 1 tablespoon almond butter

Snack

1 ounce sliced smoked turkey and 1 slice cantaloupe

Lunch

½ serving Seared Salmon BLT (page 226)

1 cup tomato or V8 juice

Snack

½ serving Seared Salmon BLT (page 226)

1 cup raw veggies

Dinner

Spicy Chickpea Curry with Cashews (page 235)

⅔ cup cooked brown rice

1 cup steamed snow peas

WEEK 1, DAY 3

Breakfast

1 cup old-fashioned oatmeal (cooked in 1 cup 2% milk) with 1 tablespoon *each* chopped almonds and apple butter

Snack

Lentil Soup with Turkey Sausage (page 225)

Lunch

Mediterranean Wrap (page 227)

1 pear

Snack

1 ounce Jarlesburg or Cheddar cheese

6 whole grain crackers

1 cup tomato or V8 juice

Dinner

Zucchini and Summer Squash Casserole (page 236)

2 cups mixed greens with Simple Vinaigrette (page 255)

1 serving Berry Fruit Salad (page 251)

WEEK 1, DAY 4

Breakfast

Tofu and Sausage Breakfast Pocket (page 222)

Snack

1 tablespoon almond or peanut butter

6 whole grain crackers

1 orange

Lunch

Quick Greek Salad (page 228)

1 serving whole wheat pita bread

Snack

Berry Fruit Salad (page 251)

1 cup cottage cheese

Dinner

Crab Cakes with Mango-Avocado Salsa (page 237)

2 cups mixed greens with Simple Vinaigrette (page 255)

Baked Fries (page 238)

WEEK 1, DAY 5

Breakfast

2 omega-3 eggs, any style

1 whole wheat English muffin, toasted

1 tablespoon butter substitute spread

2 tablespoons fruit spread or unsweetened fruit butter

Snack

$3/4$ cup high-protein cereal (such as Kashi GOLEAN Crunch!)

$3/4$ cup 2% milk

Lunch

Avocado, Cheese, and Toasted Sunflower Seed Pita Pocket (page 229)

1 cup grapes

Snack

$\frac{1}{4}$ cup prepared hummus and carrot sticks

Dinner

Shortcut Chili (page 239)

$\frac{2}{3}$ cup brown rice

1 cup salad greens and 1 cup chopped raw vegetables

1 tablespoon Simple Vinaigrette (page 255)

WEEK 1, DAY 6

Breakfast

Homemade Granola (page 220)

1 cup 2% milk

$\frac{1}{2}$ cup berries

Snack

$\frac{1}{2}$ serving Shortcut Chili (page 239)

$\frac{1}{3}$ cup brown rice

Lunch

Chicken Spinach Pita Pizza (page 230)

1 cup salad greens and 1 cup chopped raw veggies

1 tablespoon Simple Vinaigrette (page 255)

Snack

Ginger-Mango Smoothie (page 248)

Dinner

Salmon with White Beans and Watercress
(page 240)

Toasted Almond Fruit Salad (page 249)

WEEK 1, DAY 7

Breakfast

Cottage Cheese Pancakes (page 223)

$\frac{1}{2}$ cup berries

$\frac{1}{2}$ cup plain, low-fat yogurt

Snack

1 cheese stick

6 carrot sticks

Lunch

Easy Minestrone (page 231)

1 ounce cheese

2 rye crisps

Snack

1 medium apple with 3 tablespoons yogurt-peanut
butter dip (2 tablespoons low-fat yogurt mixed with
1 tablespoon natural creamy peanut butter)

Dinner

Roast Chicken with Savory (page 241)

Quinoa Salad with Cherries and Pecans (page 257)

1 cup steamed cauliflower and carrots

WEEK 2, DAY 1

Breakfast

1 serving Speedy Egg Burrito (page 221)

Snack

1 pear

1 ounce Cheddar cheese

Lunch

Easy Chef Salad (page 232)

1 slice flatbread

1 nectarine

Snack

Date-Walnut-Flaxseed Balls (page 248)

Dinner

Spicy Seafood Stew (page 242)

$2/3$ cup brown rice

6 spears steamed asparagus

WEEK 2, DAY 2

Breakfast

1 cup old-fashioned oatmeal cooked with 1 cup 2% milk

1 tablespoon chopped walnuts

1 tablespoon raisins

Snack

Easy Minestrone (page 231)

Lunch

½ grilled chicken breast sandwich on whole wheat, with omega-3 mayo, lettuce, and tomato

Red pepper slices

1 apple

Snack

½ grilled chicken breast sandwich

1 cup Berry Fruit Salad

Dinner

Spinach Lasagna (page 243)

Chopped Salad (page 250)

WEEK 2, DAY 3

Breakfast

1 cup plain low-fat yogurt with ½ banana and ½ cup Homemade Granola (page 220)

Snack

1 hard-cooked omega-3 egg, sliced

1 tablespoon Creamy Honey Mustard Dressing (page 255)

6 whole grain crackers

1 cup tomato or V8 juice

Lunch

Tuna Salad Pocket (page 232)

1 Asian pear

Carrot sticks

Snack

Spiced Nut Clusters (page 253)

Dinner

Savory Pot Roast with Vegetables (page 244)

1 cup mixed salad greens with Creamy Honey Mustard Dressing (page 255)

1 whole wheat dinner roll

1 tablespoon butter substitute spread

WEEK 2, DAY 4

Breakfast

1 serving high-protein cereal (such as Kashi GOLEAN Crunch!)

1 cup 2% milk

½ banana

Snack

Blueberry Yogurt Parfait (page 254)

Lunch

Mesclun Salad with Bacon Crumbles (page 230)

1 cup tomato soup

6 whole grain crackers

Snack

Toasted Almond Fruit Salad (page 249)

1 cup cottage cheese

Dinner

2-Minute Shrimp Scampi (page 239)

⅔ cup quick-cooking brown rice

WEEK 2, DAY 5

Breakfast

Maple Almond Smoothie (page 249)

Snack

1 hard-cooked omega-3 egg, sliced

1 tablespoon Creamy Honey Mustard Dressing (page 255)

6 whole grain crackers

Lunch

Sardine Spread (page 250)

2 rye crisps

Chopped Salad (page 250)

Date-Walnut-Flaxseed Balls (page 248)

Snack

1 cup plain low-fat yogurt

Orange and Pomegranate Salad (page 252)

Dinner

Citrus Chicken with Quinoa and Roasted Vegetables (page 245)

WEEK 2, DAY 6

Breakfast

Whole grain blueberry waffles with soy sausage

1 tablespoon maple syrup

Snack

1 ounce smoked salmon and 1 slice melon

Lunch

Avocado, Cheese, and Toasted Sunflower Seed Pita Pocket (page 229)

1 cup tomato or V8 juice

Snack

12 almonds and 2 dried apricots

Dinner

Pesto Fish with Couscous and Green Beans (page 246)

WEEK 2, DAY 7

Breakfast

Florentine Omelet (page 224)

Snack

1 cup yogurt

1 cup berries

Lunch

Cauliflower Soup with Grilled Shrimp (page 233)

1 cup mixed greens with 1 grated carrot

1 tablespoon Fabulous French Dressing (page 254)

Snack

Spiced Nut Clusters (page 253)

Dinner

Turkey Meat Loaf (page 247)

1 cup steamed broccoli with 1 tablespoon shredded Parmesan cheese

½ cup yellow corn

Orange and Pomegranate Salad (page 252)

BREAKFAST RECIPES

Homemade Granola

Double or even triple this recipe and store it in airtight containers. Soy nuts or sunflower seeds add protein to this not-too-sweet, reduced-fat granola.

    2 cups old-fashioned oats
    2 tablespoons packed brown sugar
    2 tablespoons honey
    2 teaspoons canola oil
    1 teaspoon vanilla extract
    ½ teaspoon ground cinnamon
    ⅛ teaspoon salt
    1 tablespoon ground flaxseeds
    ¼ cup roasted soy nuts or sunflower seeds

Preheat the oven to 350°F. Spread the oats in a single layer on a shallow baking pan. Bake for 18 minutes or until the oats are toasted, stirring halfway through.

Meanwhile, in a large bowl whisk together the sugar, honey, oil, vanilla, cinnamon, and salt until blended. Stir in the hot oats until they're evenly coated.

Coat the same baking pan with cooking spray. Spread the granola on it in an even layer. Bake for 15 minutes or until golden brown. Sprinkle the flaxseeds evenly on top. Cool in the pan on a rack for 30 minutes. Stir in the soy nuts or sunflower seeds.

Makes 6 servings

Per serving: 106 calories, 6 g protein, 16 g carbohydrates, 3 g fiber, 6 g fat, 0 g saturated fat, 64 mg sodium

One-Bowl Power Breakfast

Seven brainpower foods in one bowl, ready in about 5 minutes.

$\frac{1}{2}$ cup old-fashioned oats
$\frac{3}{4}$ cup 2% milk
1 omega-3 egg
$\frac{1}{2}$ cup mixed berries
1 tablespoon chopped pecans or sliced almonds
1 teaspoon ground flaxseeds
1 tablespoon plain yogurt

In a small bowl, stir together the oats and milk. Microwave for one minute; stir. Add the egg, berries, pecans, and flaxseeds and microwave for another 2 minutes, or until the egg is set. Let it cool for a minute or two. Top with the yogurt.

Makes 1 serving

Per serving: 470 calories, 22 g protein, 55 g carbohydrates, 10 g fiber, 18 g fat, 5 g saturated fat, 15 mg sodium

Speedy Egg Burrito

This burrito can travel, but it tastes great on a plate, too. Omega-3 eggs add brain-healthy fats. Protein, fiber, and two servings of vegetables give you a head start on the day's nutrition.

2 omega-3 eggs
$\frac{1}{4}$ cup frozen corn, thawed
$\frac{1}{4}$ cup black beans, rinsed and drained well
1 whole wheat tortilla (10" diameter)
$\frac{1}{4}$ cup low-fat shredded Cheddar cheese
$\frac{1}{4}$ cup salsa

In a medium bowl, beat the eggs. Stir in the corn and beans. Coat a microwavable plate with cooking spray and spread the mixture on the plate. Microwave for 1 minute. Stir with a fork, and microwave again until the eggs are cooked. Spoon into the tortilla. Top with the shredded cheese and salsa. Fold, roll, and serve.

Makes 1 serving

Per serving: 372 calories, 27 g protein, 55 g carbohydrates, 7 g fiber, 12 g fat, 4 g saturated fat, 674 mg sodium

Tofu and Sausage Breakfast Pocket

If you're short on time, use 1 cup of frozen mixed bell peppers and 1 teaspoon of dried chives in place of the bell pepper and scallion. If you have a frozen sausage patty in your freezer, partially thaw it, chop it up, and use it in place of the bulk sausage.

1 teaspoon olive oil

½ red bell pepper, chopped

2 ounces bulk soy sausage, crumbled

1 large scallion, chopped

2 ounces firm tofu, drained

¼ teaspoon dried tarragon, crumbled

Pinch of freshly ground black pepper

3 tablespoons shredded, reduced-fat Cheddar cheese

½ whole wheat pita

Heat the oil in a small nonstick skillet over medium heat. Add the bell pepper and cook, stirring occasionally, for 5 minutes or until softened. Stir in the sausage and scallion. Cook for 2 minutes or until browned. Add the tofu, tarragon, and black pepper. Cook for 2 minutes or until heated through, breaking up the tofu and stirring frequently. Stir in the cheese and cook for 2 minutes, or until melted. Spoon into the pita and serve.

Makes 1 serving

Per serving: 314 calories, 23 g protein, 26 g carbohydrates, 6 g fiber, 15 g fat, 4 g saturated fat, 487 mg sodium

Cottage Cheese Pancakes

There will be no carb-related bloating or sugar crash after you eat these high-protein, omega-3-rich pancakes.

1 cup low-fat cottage cheese

2 omega-3 eggs

2 tablespoons butter substitute spread

½ cup 2% milk

¾ cup whole wheat flour

1 tablespoon baking powder

1 tablespoon sugar

½ teaspoon nutmeg (optional)

In a large bowl, stir together the cheese, eggs, spread, and milk. Add the flour, baking powder, sugar, and nutmeg (if using), and stir until just combined. Coat a griddle with cooking spray and place it over medium heat. Drop the batter by ¼ cupfuls onto the griddle, and use the back of a spoon to spread it out evenly. Cook for 4 minutes or until small air bubbles begin to form. Flip and cook for another 2 minutes or until set.

Makes 4 servings (3 pancakes per serving)

Per serving: 223 calories, 14 g protein, 24 g carbohydrates, 3 g fiber, 9 g fat, 3 g saturated fat, 644 mg sodium

Florentine Omelet

Start your day with folate-rich spinach and a serving of omega-3 eggs to give your brain a boost.

> 2 teaspoons extra-virgin olive oil
> 2 tablespoons sliced mushrooms
> 2 tablespoons chopped onion
> 2 tablespoons chopped red bell pepper
> ½ cup packed spinach leaves, chopped
> 2 omega-3 eggs
> ½ teaspoon Italian seasoning
> 1 tablespoon water
> 2 tablespoons shredded, low-fat mozzarella cheese

Heat the oil in a skillet over medium heat. Add the mushrooms, onion, pepper, and spinach, and cook for 2 minutes, or until the vegetables begin to soften.

Whisk together the eggs, seasoning, and water. Add the egg mixture to the pan and cook until set. Top the omelet with the cheese.

Makes 1 serving

Per serving: 286 calories, 19 g protein, 6 g carbohydrates, 1 g fiber, 22 g fat, 6 g saturated fat, 338 mg sodium

LUNCH RECIPES

Lentil Soup with Turkey Sausage

This filling soup has plenty of fiber, B vitamins, complex carbohydrates, and protein.

1 tablespoon extra-virgin olive oil

1½ teaspoons whole cumin seeds

8 ounces turkey sausage, cut into ½-inch slices

1 large onion, chopped

4 cloves garlic, minced

½ teaspoon ground coriander

½ teaspoon freshly ground black pepper

1 teaspoon paprika

1⅓ cups (½ pound) lentils, sorted and rinsed

5 cups water

1 can (14½ ounces) diced tomatoes

2 cups packed, shredded, fresh spinach

½ cup unsalted peanuts, chopped

½ teaspoon salt

½ cup fat-free Greek-style yogurt

Place the oil and cumin seeds in a Dutch oven or large, heavy saucepan over medium heat. Cook, stirring, for 3 minutes, or until fragrant. Stir in the sausage, onion, garlic, coriander, and pepper. Cook, stirring often, for 4 to 6 minutes, or until the sausage is no longer pink. Stir in the paprika. Add the lentils and water.

Cover and bring to a boil. Reduce the heat to low and simmer, covered, for 30 to 35 minutes, or until the lentils are very tender. Stir in the tomatoes, spinach, peanuts, and salt. Increase the heat and simmer, uncovered, for 5 minutes longer. Garnish each serving with a heaping tablespoon of yogurt.

Makes 6 servings

Per serving: 321 calories, 22 g protein, 32 g carbohydrates, 8 g fiber, 12 g fat, 2 g saturated fat, 412 mg sodium

Seared Salmon BLT

Turkey bacon, salmon, and omega-3 mayonnaise make this a guilt-free treat. Don't overcook the salmon. It's perfectly done when it is just opaque but is still moist on the inside.

> 4 slices turkey bacon
> 4 skinless salmon fillets (3 ounces each)
> ¼ teaspoon ground black pepper
> ¼ cup omega-3 mayonnaise
> 4 slices whole wheat bread, toasted and cut in half
> 4 small Boston lettuce leaves
> 1 tomato, cut into 8 slices

Coat a medium nonstick skillet with cooking spray and place it over medium-high heat. Add the bacon and cook for 2 minutes per side, or until crisp. Transfer to a plate and set aside.

Sprinkle the salmon with the pepper and add it to the skillet. Cook for 8 minutes turning once, or until the fish flakes easily with a fork. Transfer the salmon to a plate.

Spread 1½ teaspoons of mayonnaise on each of the 8 bread halves. Arrange 4 bread halves on a work surface, mayonnaise sides up, and top each with 1 lettuce leaf, 2 tomato slices, 1 slice of bacon, and 1 salmon fillet. Set the remaining bread halves, mayonnaise sides down, over the salmon.

Makes 4 servings

Per serving: 374 calories, 24 g protein, 16 g carbohydrates, 2 g fiber, 24 g fat, 3 g saturated fat, 553 mg sodium

Mediterranean Wrap

A brain-pleasing balance of fats, protein, and carbohydrates, with a true taste of healthy Mediterranean cuisine.

 1 whole wheat wrap (10" diameter)
 2 tablespoons hummus
 1 plum tomato, seeded and chopped
 ¼ cucumber, peeled and chopped
 1 tablespoon chopped red onion
 1 tablespoon crumbled feta cheese
 1 tablespoon chopped black olives

Place the wrap on a work surface. Spread the hummus in a line across the center of the wrap, leaving a 1½-inch border at each end. Top the hummus with the tomato, cucumber, onion, cheese, and olives. Fold the right and left sides of the wrap so that they cover the edges of the filling, then fold the bottom over, and roll up burrito-style.

Makes 1 serving

Per serving: 276 calories, 9 g protein, 38 g carbohydrates, 7 g fiber, 10 g fat, 3 g saturated fat, 574 mg sodium

Quick Greek Salad

Use prewashed greens, and you can assemble this tasty salad in no time. It provides folate, vitamin C, healthy monounsaturated fats, and plenty of flavor.

  2 tablespoons balsamic vinegar
  2 teaspoons extra-virgin olive oil
  Pinch of black pepper
  5 cups mixed greens
  2 Roma tomatoes, chopped
  ½ cup cucumber, chopped
  2 tablespoons shredded mozzarella
  6 pitted Kalamata olives

In a large bowl, whisk together the vinegar, oil, and pepper. Add the greens, tomatoes, cucumber, mozzarella, and olives, and toss to coat well.

Makes 2 servings

Per serving: 293 calories, 7 g protein, 16 g carbohydrates, 5 g fiber, 23 g fat, 3 g saturated fat, 650 mg sodium

Asian Coleslaw

Crunchy, tangy, and just a little spicy—this is the healthy way to enjoy coleslaw.

  Juice of ½ lime
  2 teaspoons low-sodium soy sauce
  2 teaspoons toasted sesame oil
  ¼ teaspoon salt
  ¼ teaspoon freshly ground black pepper
  4 cups shredded green cabbage
  ½ cup finely sliced onion
  ½ cup finely sliced carrot

In a large bowl, whisk together the lime juice, soy sauce, sesame oil, salt, and pepper. Add the cabbage, onion, and carrot, and toss to coat well.

Makes 4 servings

Per serving: 55 calories, 1 g protein, 8 g carbohydrates, 2 g fiber, 2 g fat, 0 g saturated fat, 258 mg sodium

Avocado, Cheese, and Toasted Sunflower Seed Pita Pocket

Use perfectly ripe Hass avocados (the small, pear-shaped kind) for a creamy, rich sandwich. Avocados are rich in monounsaturated fats, vitamin E, potassium, and fiber. They also have beta-sitosterol, a natural substance shown to significantly lower blood cholesterol levels.

½ ripe avocado, mashed or cubed
2 ounces low-fat Cheddar cheese, shredded
1 tablespoon toasted, salted sunflower seeds
1 tablespoon balsamic vinegar
1 large whole wheat pita, sliced in half to form 2 pockets
Shredded lettuce
Sliced tomato
Diced red onion

In a medium bowl, toss together the avocado, cheese, sunflower seeds, and vinegar. Stuff the mixture into the pita halves with the lettuce, tomato, and onion.

Makes 1 serving

Per serving: 364 calories, 13 g protein, 45 g carbohydrates, 10 g fiber, 17 g fat, 3 g saturated fat, 435 mg sodium

Chicken Spinach Pita Pizza

You'll love this quick, tasty pizza with lots of lean protein and folate-rich spinach.

> 1 large whole wheat pita
> 3 tablespoons marinara sauce
> ⅓ cup frozen spinach, thawed and drained
> ¼ cup crumbled feta cheese
> ¾ cup chopped cooked chicken breast
> Pepper

Preheat the oven to 375°F.

Place the pita on a baking sheet and spread it with the marinara. Top with the spinach, cheese, and chicken. Season with the pepper to taste. Bake for 6 minutes.

Makes 1 serving

Per serving: 392 calories, 44 g protein, 35 g carbohydrates, 7 g fiber, 9 g fat, 3 g saturated fat, 663 mg sodium

Mesclun Salad with Bacon Crumbles

Beans and greens are a perfect combination of nutrients needed for proper brain function: amino acids like tyrosine, lots of B vitamins, magnesium, and healthy fats. Plus, this salad is full of fiber.

> 2 cups mixed salad greens
> ½ cup red kidney beans, rinsed and drained
> 1 tablespoon minced red onion
> 2 tablespoons minced green pepper
> 1 tablespoon soy or turkey bacon crumbles
> 1 tablespoon Simple Vinaigrette (page 255)

In a medium bowl, combine the greens, beans, onion, pepper, bacon, and vinaigrette. Toss to coat well.

Makes 1 serving

Per serving: 243 calories, 14 g protein, 39 g carbohydrates, 15 g fiber, 5 g fat, 0 g saturated fat, 460 mg sodium

Easy Minestrone

Beans and lots of vegetables make this classic Italian soup a light but filling lunchtime favorite.

1 tablespoon extra-virgin olive oil

3 ribs celery, chopped

1 onion, chopped

2 cups water

2 cups low-sodium chicken broth

1 can (28 ounces) whole tomatoes, chopped, juice reserved

2 teaspoons dried basil

2 teaspoons chopped parsley

1 teaspoon dried oregano

½ teaspoon black pepper

1 bay leaf

2 medium potatoes, chopped

2 medium carrots, chopped

2 cans (15 ounces each) kidney beans, rinsed and drained

½ cup small shell pasta, uncooked

Parmesan cheese

Heat the oil in a medium saucepan over medium heat. Add the celery and onion and cook for 10 minutes, or until soft but not brown. Add the water, broth, tomatoes and juice, basil, parsley, oregano, pepper, and bay leaf. Bring to a boil.

Reduce the heat to low, cover, and simmer for 25 minutes. Add the potatoes and carrots, cover, and simmer for 15 minutes, or until the vegetables are tender. Add the beans and pasta and cook for 12 minutes, or until the pasta is al dente. Remove and discard the bay leaf. Serve with a sprinkling of cheese.

Makes 6 servings

Per serving: 262 calories, 13 g protein, 47 g carbohydrates, 11 g fiber, 4 g fat, 1 g saturated fat, 560 mg sodium

Easy Chef Salad

Tuna or salmon and chickpeas make a great combination in this quick, protein-packed salad.

    2 cups mixed salad greens
    2 ounces water-packed canned tuna or salmon, drained
    ¼ cup cooked chickpeas
    2 tablespoons shredded reduced-fat cheese
    2 tablespoons reduced-fat ranch dressing

In a medium bowl, toss the greens, tuna or salmon, chickpeas, cheese, and dressing until well blended.

Makes 1 serving

Per serving: 243 calories, 22 g protein, 22 g carbohydrates, 4 g fiber, 8 g fat, 2 g saturated fat, 689 mg sodium

Tuna Salad Pocket

The combination of tuna and omega-3 mayonnaise makes this an excellent lunch, because it's packed with healthy fats.

    4 ounces chunk light tuna, packed in water, drained
    1 tablespoon omega-3 mayonnaise
    2 tablespoons minced celery
    1 whole wheat pita, sliced in half

In a small bowl, combine the tuna, mayonnaise, and celery. Stuff each pita half with half of the tuna mixture.

Makes 1 serving

Per serving: 412 calories, 36 g protein, 36 g carbohydrates, 5 g fiber, 13 g fat, 2 g saturated fat, 885 mg sodium

Cauliflower Soup with Grilled Shrimp

Make this soup ahead of time and enjoy it as a light, satisfying lunch. Use frozen shrimp that are already peeled and deveined. If you're short on time, microwave the shrimp instead of grilling them. Omega-3s, fiber, folate, vitamin B_6, vitamin C, and protein make this good brain food.

    3 teaspoons olive oil
    1 red onion, chopped
    2 ribs celery, chopped
    4 cups cauliflower florets
    $1/2$ teaspoon ground coriander
    2 cans (14.5 ounces each) reduced-sodium chicken broth
    $2^1/2$ cups water
    12 ounces large shrimp, peeled and deveined
    $1/4$ teaspoon salt
    $1/4$ teaspoon ground black pepper
    $1/3$ cup 2% milk

Coat a grill rack with cooking spray. Preheat the grill to medium-high.

Heat 2 teaspoons of the oil in a large saucepan over medium heat. Add the onion and celery. Cook, stirring occasionally, for 6 minutes, or until lightly browned. Stir in the cauliflower and coriander and cook for 2 minutes. Add the broth and water and bring to a boil. Reduce the heat to medium-low. Cover and simmer for 20 minutes, or until the cauliflower is tender. Remove from the heat and let cool for 5 minutes.

Season the shrimp with $1/8$ teaspoon of the salt, $1/8$ teaspoon of the pepper, and the remaining 1 teaspoon of oil. Grill for 5 minutes, turning once, until the shrimp are opaque. In a blender or food processor, puree the soup in batches. Return it to the pan. Stir in the milk and the remaining $1/8$ teaspoon of salt and $1/8$ teaspoon of pepper. Warm the soup over medium heat until heated through. To serve, ladle the soup into bowls and top with the shrimp.

Makes 4 servings

Per serving: 214 calories, 25 g protein, 15 g carbohydrates, 5 g fiber, 7 g fat, 1 g saturated fat, 414 mg sodium

DINNER RECIPES

Flounder with Lemon Broccoli and Bulgur

You can assemble this dish ahead of time, cover and refrigerate it for a day or two, and then just bake it in a preheated oven when you're ready for it. This recipe contains a good balance of protein, whole grain carbohydrates, healthy fats, and folate-rich veggies.

1 lemon
2 large heads of broccoli, cut into florets
4 flounder fillets (4–6 ounces each)
2 tablespoons whole wheat pastry flour
$\frac{3}{4}$ cup 2% milk
$\frac{1}{2}$ cup shredded Cheddar cheese
Pinch of paprika
2 cups hot, cooked bulgur

Preheat the oven to 350°F. Coat an 8" x 8" baking dish with cooking spray. Grate $\frac{1}{2}$ teaspoon of lemon zest into a large bowl. Halve the lemon and squeeze the juice into the bowl. Set aside.

Place a steamer basket in a saucepan filled with 1 inch of water. Add the broccoli and bring the water to a boil over high heat. Cover and steam for 6 minutes, or until tender-crisp. Rinse under cold water and drain well. Add the broccoli to the bowl with the lemon juice.

Cut each fillet in half across its width. Arrange 4 pieces in the bottom of the baking dish. Divide the broccoli among the pieces and spread it in an even layer. Top with the remaining fillet pieces.

Place the flour in a small saucepan. Slowly whisk in the milk to make a smooth mixture. Cook over medium heat, whisking constantly, for 5 minutes or until thickened. Remove from the heat and stir in the cheese. Pour the cheese sauce over the fillets. Sprinkle with the paprika. Bake for 25 minutes, or until the fish flakes easily. Serve with the bulgur.

Makes 4 servings

Per serving: 350 calories, 42 g protein, 28 g carbohydrates, 7 g fiber, 8 g fat, 4 g saturated fat, 374 mg sodium

Spicy Chickpea Curry with Cashews

Chickpeas are a good source of vitamin B_6, a nutrient needed for proper neurotransmitter production. And the turmeric in curry is one of the best brain cell protectors there is. Great for busy weeknights, you can prepare this dish in just 15 minutes.

>   1 tablespoon cornstarch
>   1 cup low-sodium vegetable broth
>   2 teaspoons extra-virgin olive oil
>   ½ onion, chopped
>   2 teaspoons curry powder
>   ¼ teaspoon salt
>   ¼ teaspoon freshly ground black pepper
>   1 can (15 ounces) no-salt-added chickpeas, rinsed and drained
>   ½ cup unsalted cashews, coarsely chopped
>   ¼ cup chopped fresh cilantro
>   4 tablespoons 0% Greek yogurt

In a small bowl, whisk the cornstarch with just enough of the broth to dissolve it. Set aside.

In a large skillet over medium heat, combine the oil, onion, curry powder, salt, and pepper. Cover and cook, stirring occasionally, for 5 minutes, or until the onion is softened. Add the remaining broth to the pan, along with the reserved cornstarch mixture. Cook, whisking constantly, until thickened. Add the chickpeas and cashews. Simmer for 5 minutes to allow the flavors to blend. Stir in the cilantro. Serve with a dollop of the yogurt.

Makes 4 servings

Per serving: 172 calories, 9 g protein, 26 g carbohydrates, 6 g fiber, 4 g fat, 1 g saturated fat, 195 mg sodium

Zucchini and Summer Squash Casserole

Here's a delicious way to use the summer's bounty. Feel free to use all zucchini or summer squash if desired.

1 tablespoon extra-virgin olive oil

1 small onion, thinly sliced

1 pound (about 3 medium) zucchini, sliced into thin rounds

1 pound (about 3 medium) yellow summer squash, sliced into thin rounds

1 clove garlic, minced

1 teaspoon chopped fresh parsley

1 teaspoon chopped fresh thyme

2 omega-3 eggs

¼ cup 2% milk

½ cup crushed whole grain crackers

¼ cup grated Parmesan cheese

Preheat the oven to 350°F. Coat a 13" x 9" baking dish with cooking spray.

Heat the oil in a medium saucepan over medium-high heat. Add the onion, pepper, and cook for 5 minutes, or until the onion is soft. Add the zucchini, squash, and garlic and cook for 20 minutes, or until the squash is tender. Stir in the parsley and thyme and remove the saucepan from the heat. Use a slotted spoon to transfer the vegetables to the prepared baking dish. Reserve the cooking liquid.

In a medium bowl, whisk together the eggs, milk, and reserved cooking liquid. Pour the mixture over the vegetables in the baking dish. Bake for 30 minutes, or until a knife inserted in the center comes out clean. Remove from the oven and sprinkle with the cracker crumbs and cheese. Return to the oven and bake for 10 minutes, or until golden brown.

Makes 2 servings

Per serving: 350 calories, 19 g protein, 35 g carbohydrates, 8 g fiber, 18 g fat, 5 g saturated fat, 287 mg sodium

Crab Cakes with Mango-Avocado Salsa

Crabmeat is a good source of omega-3s and trace minerals important for brain function, such as zinc, iron, and copper. If you don't like or don't have mangoes, improvise a healthy tartar sauce by mixing equal parts mayo and plain yogurt with chopped pickles, capers, and fresh lemon juice.

> 1 can (16 ounces) jumbo lump crabmeat
> 2 tablespoons minced jalapeño (wear plastic gloves when handling)
> 2 scallions, chopped
> ½ cup minced red bell pepper
> 1 omega-3 egg, lightly beaten
> 2 teaspoons Dijon mustard
> Juice of 1 lemon
> ¼ teaspoon crab boil seasoning
> ½ teaspoon salt
> ¾ cup dry bread crumbs
> Mango-Avocado Salsa (see page 238)

Preheat the oven to 425°F. Coat a nonstick baking sheet or a baking dish with cooking spray. In a large bowl, combine the crab, jalapeño, scallions, pepper, egg, mustard, lemon juice, seasoning, salt, and ¼ cup of the bread crumbs. Gently stir with a rubber spatula. Using your hands, loosely form the crab mixture into 8 patties.

Spread the remaining ½ cup of bread crumbs on a plate and roll each crab cake over the crumbs to lightly and evenly coat. As the cakes are formed, place them on the baking sheet or in the baking dish. Bake for 12 to 15 minutes, turning once, or until golden brown on the outside. Serve with a scoop of Mango-Avocado Salsa.

Makes 4 servings

Per serving: 273 calories, 25 g protein, 27 g carbohydrates, 4 g fiber, 7 g fat, 1 g saturated fat, 527 mg sodium

Mango-Avocado Salsa

Turn any fish or seafood into an antioxidant-rich tropical treat with this colorful salsa.

> 1 ripe mango, chopped
> 1 ripe Hass avocado, chopped
> ⅓ ripe pineapple, chopped
> ¼ red onion, minced
> 1 tablespoon fresh cilantro, minced
> 1 tablespoon fresh lime juice
> ¼ teaspoon salt

In a large bowl, combine the mango, avocado, pineapple, onion, cilantro, lime juice, and salt. Toss to coat well. Refrigerate until ready to serve.

Makes 4 servings

Per serving: 156 calories, 2 g protein, 24 g carbohydrates, 4 g fiber, 7 g fat, 1 g saturated fat, 151 mg sodium

Baked Fries

If you like French fries, these are a great substitute—with less fat, no trans fats, and no brain-clogging oxidized fat from an overheated deep fryer!

> 2 large Yukon gold potatoes, scrubbed and cut lengthwise into
>   ½" strips
> 3 tablespoons extra-virgin olive oil
> ½ teaspoon salt
> Cracked black pepper

Preheat the oven to 350°F. Cover a baking sheet with foil and coat the foil with cooking spray.

Toss the potato strips, oil, salt, and pepper to taste on the baking sheet. Spread the fries in a single layer, and bake for 45 minutes, turning once, or until brown and crisp on both sides.

Makes 2 servings

Per serving: 289 calories, 3 g protein, 26 g carbohydrates, 2 g fiber, 20 g fat, 3 g saturated fat, 581 mg sodium

Shortcut Chili

This dish takes about half an hour, start to finish. Use grass-fed beef for an added dose of omega-3s.

> 8 ounces lean ground beef
> 2 cans (16 ounces each) no-salt-added diced tomatoes, drained
> 1 jar (8 ounces) salsa
> 1 can (15 ounces) kidney beans, rinsed and drained
> 1 teaspoon chili powder

Crumble the beef into a large nonstick skillet placed over medium-high heat. Cook, breaking up the beef with a wooden spoon, for 5 minutes, or until it's browned. Stir in the tomatoes, salsa, beans, and chili powder. Cover and bring to a boil. Reduce the heat to low and simmer for 10 minutes, stirring occasionally.

Makes 4 servings

Per serving: 330 calories, 29 g protein, 25 g carbohydrates, 7 g fiber, 12 g fat, 5 g saturated fat, 560 mg sodium

2-Minute Shrimp Scampi

This is the dish to pick when you think you don't have time to make a healthy meal.

> 24 large frozen shrimp (peeled and deveined)
> 2 cups spinach leaves, chopped
> 2 cloves garlic, crushed
> 1/2 teaspoon dried basil
> 1 teaspoon extra-virgin olive oil
> 1/2 teaspoon hot sauce

In a microwaveable bowl, combine the shrimp, spinach, garlic, basil, oil, and hot sauce. Microwave on high for 1 minute. Remove and toss well. Microwave on high for 1 minute more, or until the shrimp are opaque.

Makes 2 servings

Per serving: 224 calories, 18 g protein, 5 g carbohydrates, 1 g fiber, 15 g fat, 2 g saturated fat, 171 mg sodium

Salmon with White Beans and Watercress

This easy-to-make dish has just about everything your body needs: omega-3s, protein, vitamins B_{12} and B_6, folate, and fiber. As if that wasn't enough, watercress is also a member of the cancer-fighting cruciferous family of vegetables.

> 4 salmon fillets (4 ounces each)
> Salt
> Ground black pepper
> 1¼ cups water
> 2 cloves garlic, minced
> 1 can (15 ounces) cannellini beans, rinsed and drained
> 4 plum tomatoes, diced
> ½ cup reduced-sodium low-fat chicken broth
> 1 bunch watercress, rinsed and coarsely chopped
> ¼ cup chopped fresh parsley

Coat a broiler pan with cooking spray. Preheat the broiler. Season the salmon fillets with the salt and pepper, and place them on the broiler pan. Broil 4 inches from the heat for 6 minutes, turning once, or until just opaque.

Place the water in a large nonstick skillet and bring it to a boil over medium-high heat. Add the garlic and cook, stirring, for 1 minute. Add the beans, tomatoes, and broth. Cook, stirring occasionally, for 4 minutes, or until heated through. Add the watercress and parsley. Cook for 30 seconds, or until the watercress begins to wilt. Divide among 4 plates. Top each with a salmon filet.

Makes 4 servings

Per serving: 290 calories, 27 g protein, 15 g carbohydrates, 4 g fiber, 15 g fat, 2 g saturated fat, 317 mg sodium

Roast Chicken with Savory

Organic chicken is sweet and juicy, so if you've never had it before, you're in for a treat. This dish is easy to prepare, and once it gets cooking, it will fill your kitchen with a mouthwatering aroma. Great for a weekend evening meal.

  1 organic chicken (about 5 pounds), washed and patted dry
  1 large handful winter savory
  1 head garlic, cut in half vertically
  2 tablespoons extra-virgin olive oil
  Pinch coarse sea salt
  Pinch freshly ground black pepper

Preheat the oven to 425°F.

Stuff the chicken with the savory and garlic. (The entire cavity should be filled, and savory should not stick out.) Place the chicken breast-side-up on a roasting rack in a baking pan. Rub the exterior of the chicken with the olive oil, and sprinkle it with the salt and pepper.

Roast for 1 to 1½ hours, or until a thermometer inserted in a breast registers 180°F and the juices run clear. Let stand for 10 minutes before carving. Discard the skin before eating.

Makes 4 servings

Per serving: 420 calories, 62 g protein, 5 g carbohydrates, 2 g fiber, 15 g fat, 3 g saturated fat, 327 mg sodium

Spicy Seafood Stew

Scallops, shrimp, and clams add up to lots of omega-3s in this colorful stew.

>   1 tablespoon extra-virgin olive oil
>   1 medium onion, chopped
>   1 small red bell pepper, chopped
>   1 clove garlic, minced
>   1 can (28 ounces) diced tomatoes with juice
>   1 can (28 ounces) low-sodium tomato sauce
>   ¼ cup dry red wine
>   ¼ cup chopped fresh parsley
>   2 teaspoons dried oregano
>   1 teaspoon Worcestershire sauce
>   ¼ teaspoon crushed red pepper flakes
>   8 ounces bay scallops
>   8 ounces medium shrimp, peeled and deveined
>   1 can (10 ounces) whole baby clams

Heat the oil in a large stockpot over medium-high heat. Add the onion, bell pepper, and garlic. Cook, stirring frequently, for 5 minutes, or until the onion is tender. Stir in the tomatoes with juice, tomato sauce, wine, parsley, oregano, Worcestershire sauce, and red pepper flakes.

Bring the mixture to a boil over medium heat. Reduce the heat to low, cover, and simmer, stirring occasionally, for 20 minutes. Add the scallops, shrimp, and clams. Return to a simmer. Cook, stirring, for 8 minutes or until the seafood is opaque.

Makes 6 servings

Per serving: 260 calories, 31 g protein, 22 g carbohydrates, 5 g fiber, 6 g fat, 1 g saturated fat, 391 mg sodium

Spinach Lasagna

Folate-packed spinach, whole wheat noodles, and fat-free ricotta make this a superhealthy treat. This is a good dish to make ahead of time and then reheat.

2 cups fat-free ricotta cheese

1 package (10 ounces) frozen chopped spinach, thawed and squeezed dry

1 omega-3 egg

1 teaspoon dried basil

½ teaspoon Italian seasoning

½ teaspoon salt

¼ teaspoon black pepper

2 cups part-skim mozzarella cheese

1 jar (28 ounces) spaghetti sauce

6 whole wheat lasagna noodles, uncooked

1 cup water

Preheat the oven to 350°F.

In a medium bowl, combine the ricotta, spinach, egg, basil, seasoning, salt, pepper, and 1 cup of the mozzarella.

Evenly spread one-third of the sauce in a 13" x 9" baking dish. Top with 3 lasagna noodles. Spread half of the cheese mixture over the noodles. Repeat. Top with the remaining one-third of sauce and the remaining 1 cup of mozzarella. Pour the water in at the corners of the baking dish. Cover tightly with foil. Bake for 1 hour and 15 minutes, or until it's hot and bubbly and a knife inserted in the center comes out hot.

Makes 8 servings

Per serving: 304 calories, 19 g protein, 36 g carbohydrates, 3 g fiber, 8 g fat, 4 g saturated fat, 717 mg sodium

Savory Pot Roast with Vegetables

Come home to the welcoming aroma of a home-cooked meal when you start the day by assembling this classic dinner in a slow cooker. Open a bagged salad, and dinner is ready in no time!

½ cup whole grain pastry flour
1 can (14 ounces) reduced-sodium beef broth
3 tablespoons tomato paste
1 teaspoon dried thyme
1 teaspoon salt
1 teaspoon black pepper
2½ pounds boneless beef chuck roast or top sirloin roast
8 ounces baby carrots
4 ribs celery, chopped
1 cup chopped onion
1 pound small new potatoes

Coat a 4- to 6-quart slow cooker with cooking spray. Add the flour and gradually pour in the broth, whisking it constantly until smooth. Whisk in the tomato paste, thyme, salt, and pepper. Add the beef, carrots, celery, onion, and potatoes to the cooker. Spoon some of the sauce over the beef.

Cover and cook on high for 4 to 4½ hours or on low for 8 hours, or until the meat is tender.

Makes 6 servings

Per serving: 392 calories, 48 g protein, 25 g carbohydrates, 3 g fiber, 10 g fat, 3 g saturated fat, 351 mg sodium

Citrus Chicken with Quinoa and Vegetables

Fragrant, colorful, healthy, and easy to make. For even more flavor, start marinating the chicken the night before.

1/4 cup orange juice
1 tablespoon lemon juice
1 tablespoon lime juice
1/2 teaspoon dried thyme
4 boneless, skinless chicken breasts (about 4 ounces each)
1 1/2 cups reduced-sodium chicken broth
1 cup quinoa, rinsed
2 red peppers, halved
2 large onions, each cut into 4 thick slices

Combine the orange juice, lemon juice, lime juice, and thyme in a large resealable bag. Add the chicken breasts, seal the bag, and refrigerate for at least 15 minutes or as long as 8 hours.

When you're ready to serve the dish, bring the chicken broth to a boil in a small saucepan over medium-high heat. Stir in the quinoa and reduce the heat to low. Cover and simmer for 20 minutes, or until all the liquid is absorbed.

Preheat the grill or broiler. Remove the chicken from the marinade and grill or broil it, turning once, for about 15 minutes. The chicken is done when a thermometer inserted in the thickest portion registers 160°F and the juices run clear. While the chicken cooks, grill or broil the peppers and onions for 7 minutes, turning once, until browned and tender. Divide the chicken breasts, peppers, onions, and quinoa among 4 plates.

Makes 4 servings

Per serving: 345 calories, 35 g protein, 41 g carbohydrates, 6 g fiber, 4 g fat, 1 g saturated fat, 289 mg sodium

Pesto Fish with Couscous and Green Beans

Cooking with pesto—a mix of basil, olive oil, garlic, pine nuts, and Parmesan cheese—is a good way to enjoy the mood-elevating taste of fresh basil year-round.

> 4 cod fillets (about 6 ounces each)
> 4 tablespoons prepared pesto
> 2 cups reduced sodium chicken broth
> 1⅓ cups whole wheat couscous
> ½ teaspoon salt
> 1 pound green beans, steamed

Preheat the oven to 400°F. Coat a baking sheet with cooking spray.

Place the cod fillets on the prepared baking sheet and brush with the pesto. Bake for 6 to 8 minutes, or until the fish flakes easily.

Meanwhile, in a small saucepan, bring the broth, couscous, and salt to a boil over high heat. Remove from the heat, cover, and let stand for 5 minutes. Serve the cod with the couscous and steamed green beans.

Makes 4 servings

Per serving: 373 calories, 39 g protein, 40 g carbohydrates, 9 g fiber, 7 g fat, 1 g saturated fat, 66 mg sodium

Turkey Meat Loaf

Turkey is a good source of the amino acid tryptophan, a precursor to serotonin, one of the brain's important calming neurotransmitters.

$\frac{1}{2}$ cup walnuts

2 slices whole wheat bread

2 teaspoons extra-virgin olive oil

1 large carrot, grated

4 scallions, thinly sliced

1 clove garlic, minced

$\frac{1}{4}$ cup 2% milk

2 eggs, lightly beaten

1 pound ground turkey breast

$\frac{1}{4}$ cup chopped, fresh, flat-leaf parsley

$\frac{1}{4}$ cup grated Parmesan cheese

1 teaspoon dried sage

$\frac{1}{2}$ teaspoon salt

$\frac{1}{2}$ teaspoon freshly ground black pepper

Preheat the oven to 350°F. Line a rimmed baking sheet with foil and coat it with olive oil spray. Chop the walnuts in a food processor. Break up the bread and add it to the walnuts. Pulse until both are ground to fine crumbs. Transfer to a large bowl.

Heat the oil in a small nonstick skillet over medium heat. Add the carrot, scallions, and garlic and cook, stirring often, for 3 minutes, or until tender. Remove from the heat.

With a fork, stir the milk and eggs into the bread crumb mixture. Add the turkey, parsley, cheese, sage, salt, pepper, and carrot mixture. Mix gently just until blended. On the baking sheet, shape the turkey mixture into a loaf about 7" long and 4½" wide. Bake for 50 minutes, or until a thermometer inserted in the center registers 165°F and the meat is no longer pink. Let stand for 10 minutes before slicing.

Makes 4 servings

Per serving: 351 calories, 37 g protein, 14 g carbohydrates, 3 g fiber, 18 g fat, 3 g saturated fat, 570 mg sodium

SNACKS, SALADS, AND SIDE DISHES

Date-Walnut-Flaxseed Balls

Dates provide all the sugar you need to sweeten these treats, plus trace minerals and fiber. The walnuts and flax meal are good sources of healthy fats. If the mixture is dry, add some water until it's moist enough to hold together.

    1 cup walnuts
    2 cups dried dates, pitted
    ½ cup ground flaxseeds
    ¼ cup unsweetened coconut flakes, finely chopped

Pulse the walnuts in a food processor until finely chopped. Add the dates and the flaxseeds and process until the mixture forms a ball. Roll into 30 walnut-size balls. Press some coconut flakes onto the surface of each ball.

Makes 30 servings

Per serving: 76 calories, 2 g protein, 10 g carbohydrates, 3 g fiber, 4 g fat, 0 g saturated fat, 0 mg sodium

Ginger-Mango Smoothie

A delicious mid-afternoon pick-me-up, this smoothie makes a great breakfast drink as well.

    1 cup low-fat vanilla yogurt
    1 cup peeled and chopped mango (about ½)
    4 ounces soft tofu
    2 tablespoons ground flaxseeds
    1 teaspoon finely chopped crystallized ginger
    1 teaspoon flaxseed oil
    Pinch of cardamom

Combine the yogurt, mango, tofu, flaxseeds, ginger, oil, and cardamom in a blender. Puree until smooth.

Makes 2 servings

Per serving: 239 calories, 12 g protein, 30 g carbohydrates, 3 g fiber, 9 g fat, 2 g saturated fat, 87 mg sodium

Maple Almond Smoothie

This makes a nice afternoon snack. It supplies calming calcium and magnesium, healthy fats from flaxseeds and almonds, and a good amount of fiber.

    ½ cup plain, low-fat yogurt
    1 tablespoon natural almond butter
    1 tablespoon maple syrup
    1 tablespoon ground flaxseeds
    1 cup 2% milk

Combine the yogurt, almond butter, syrup, flaxseeds, and milk in a blender. Pulse until smooth and frothy.

Makes 1 serving

Per serving: 349 calories, 19 g protein, 40 g carbohydrates, 7 g fiber, 14 g fat, 4 g saturated fat, 177 mg sodium

Toasted Almond Fruit Salad

This colorful and delightful medley qualifies as a dessert—without any brain-dulling added sugar!

    3 oranges
    1 red grapefruit
    3 kiwifruit, peeled and cut into half-moon slices
    2 tablespoons dried cherries or cranberries
    2 tablespoons slivered almonds, toasted

With a serrated knife, cut the skin and white pith from the oranges and grapefruit. Working over a bowl, cut between the membranes, letting the fruit sections drop into the bowl. Squeeze the juice from the membranes into the bowl. Add the kiwi and cherries or cranberries and toss gently. Divide the fruit salad among 4 bowls and garnish with the almonds.

Makes 4 servings

Per serving: 140 calories, 3 g protein, 31 g carbohydrates, 5 g fiber, 2 g fat, 0 g saturated fat, 3 mg sodium

Sardine Spread

If you like sardines, you'll want to try this lively, satisfying snack. It's a great source of brain-healthy omega-3s.

    1 can (3.75 ounces) oil-packed sardines, drained
    1 tablespoon stone-ground mustard
    1 tablespoon finely chopped red onion
    1 tablespoon finely chopped fresh parsley
    1/4 teaspoon paprika
    1/8 teaspoon ground red pepper (optional)

In a medium bowl, mash the sardines with a fork. Stir in the mustard, onion, parsley, paprika, and pepper, if using. Serve on crackers or toast.

Makes 2 servings

Per serving: 103 calories, 12 g protein, 1 g carbohydrates, 0 g fiber, 6 g fat, 1 g saturated fat, 341 mg sodium

Chopped Salad

This is a great way to use ripe tomatoes and an easy way to add some healthy raw veggies to your day. This salad keeps well.

    1 large red tomato, chopped
    1 cucumber, peeled and chopped
    1 red bell pepper, chopped
    2 celery ribs, chopped
    2 scallions, finely sliced
    1/4 cup fresh parsley, chopped
    2 tablespoons Simple Vinaigrette (page 255)

Combine the tomato, cucumber, pepper, celery, scallions, and parsley in a large bowl. Drizzle with the vinaigrette and toss to coat well.

Makes 4 servings

Per serving: 90 calories, 1 g protein, 6 g carbohydrates, 2 g fiber, 7 g fat, 1 g saturated fat, 150 mg sodium

Berry Fruit Salad

Enjoy the natural sweetness of berries. Blueberries and raspberries are more than just tasty, though—they also contain compounds that help protect your brain from stress.

 ½ cup low-fat vanilla yogurt
 ½ teaspoon lime zest
 ½ cup blueberries
 ½ cup raspberries
 ½ cup halved strawberries
 1 tablespoon chopped fresh mint
 2 teaspoons chopped crystallized ginger
 2 tablespoons chopped walnuts

In a small bowl, combine the yogurt and lime zest. In a serving bowl, combine the blueberries, raspberries, strawberries, mint, and ginger. Toss to combine well. Top with the yogurt mixture and sprinkle with the walnuts.

Makes 2 servings

Per serving: 140 calories, 5 g protein, 19 g carbohydrates, 4 g fiber, 6 g fat, 1 g saturated fat, 43 mg sodium

Orange and Pomegranate Salad

This lovely fruit salad is high in brain-protecting antioxidants, healthy fats, and vitamin E. It keeps well for several days.

    ¼ cup maple syrup
    1 teaspoon rum-flavored extract
    ¼ teaspoon cinnamon
    4 large oranges
    ¼ cup walnut pieces, toasted
    ½ cup pomegranate seeds

In a large bowl, mix together the maple syrup, extract, and cinnamon. Peel the oranges and cut into ¼" slices. Add the orange slices to the bowl. Toss gently to coat. Refrigerate for 1 hour or overnight.

Arrange the orange sections in individual dessert bowls or on plates, drizzle each serving with 1 tablespoon of the marinade, and sprinkle with the walnuts and pomegranate seeds.

Makes 4 servings

Per serving: 182 calories, 3 g protein, 35 g carbohydrates, 4 g fiber, 5 g fat, 1 g saturated fat, 4 mg sodium

Spiced Nut Clusters

Nuts, especially walnuts, contain brain-healthy fats, including vitamin E. Cinnamon helps control blood sugar, and ginger is a great anti-inflammatory.

    1 large egg white
    1 tablespoon honey
    1 cup walnuts
    $\frac{1}{2}$ cup raw pumpkin seeds (pepitas)
    $\frac{1}{3}$ cup dried cranberries
    1 teaspoon ground cinnamon
    1 teaspoon ground ginger
    $\frac{1}{4}$ teaspoon ground cardamom

Preheat the oven to 350°F. Line a baking sheet with parchment paper.

In a medium bowl, whisk together the egg white and honey. Add the walnuts, pumpkin seeds, and cranberries. Sprinkle with the cinnamon, ginger, and cardamom and toss to coat well. Drop by $\frac{1}{8}$-cup measures onto the prepared baking sheet. Bake for 18 minutes, or until browned. Let stand on a rack for 30 minutes, or until completely cooled.

Makes 16 servings (1 cluster per serving)

Per serving: 91 calories, 4 g protein, 5 g carbohydrates, 1 g fiber, 7 g fat, 1 g saturated fat, 5 mg sodium

Blueberry Yogurt Parfait

This perfect snack or dessert couldn't be simpler. The cereal adds extra protein and a nice crunch, and blueberries help protect brain cells from stress. If fresh berries are not in season, frozen berries are fine.

> ½ cup low-fat plain yogurt
> 1 teaspoon lemon juice
> ½ cup blueberries
> ¼ cup Kashi GoLean cereal

In a small bowl, combine the yogurt and lemon juice. Layer the yogurt, blueberries, and cereal in 2 parfait glasses.

Makes 2 servings

Per serving: 156 calories, 10 g protein, 26 g carbohydrates, 4 g fiber, 2 g fat, 1 g saturated fat, 108 mg sodium

Fabulous French Dressing

So many prepared salad dressings have high-fructose corn syrup or corn oil that it's worth making your own healthier versions.

> 8 ounces red wine vinegar
> 4 teaspoons Dijon mustard
> ½ teaspoon salt
> 1 teaspoon red pepper sauce
> ⅛ teaspoon ground red pepper
> 1 teaspoon garlic powder
> ¼ teaspoon paprika
> ⅔ cup olive oil

In a 1-quart jar with a tight-fitting lid, combine the vinegar, mustard, salt, red pepper sauce, ground red pepper, garlic powder, and paprika. Cover and shake well. Add the oil, cover, and shake well again. Store in the refrigerator for up to 4 weeks.

Makes 10 servings (2 tablespoons per serving)

Per serving: 133 calories, 0 g protein, 1 g carbohydrates, 0 g fiber, 14 g fat, 2 g saturated fat, 169 mg sodium

Creamy Honey Mustard Dressing

No high-fructose corn syrup in this simple dressing—just a bit of real honey.

    2 tablespoons 0% plain Greek yogurt
    1 teaspoon spicy brown or Dijon mustard
    1 teaspoon honey
    1 teaspoon white wine vinegar

In a small bowl, combine the yogurt, mustard, honey, and vinegar. Stir until well blended.

Makes 1 serving

Per serving: 34 calories, 1 g protein, 8 g carbohydrates, 0 g fiber, 0 g fat, 0 g saturated fat, 82 mg sodium

Simple Vinaigrette

Avoid store-bought salad dressings full of sugar, salt, and extra calories. This recipe is perfect for a variety of salads such as green, potato, pasta, or bean. Feel free to change it up by using citrus juice or balsamic vinegar in place of the red wine vinegar. Add your favorite herbs and a touch of honey, if desired.

    ½ cup extra-virgin olive oil
    3 tablespoons red wine vinegar
    1 teaspoon Dijon mustard
    ¼ teaspoon salt
    ¼ teaspoon ground black pepper

In a jar with a tight-fitting lid, combine the oil, vinegar, mustard, salt, and pepper. Cover and shake well. Store in the refrigerator for up to 4 weeks.

Makes 6 servings (2 tablespoons per serving)

Per serving: 171 calories, 0 g protein, 0 g carbohydrates, 0 g fiber, 19 g fat, 3 g saturated fat, 118 mg sodium

Orange-Scented Cucumber Salad

This refreshing side salad is virtually fat-free and incredibly low in calories. Plus, the orange provides stress-fighting vitamin C.

    1 navel orange
    1 cucumber, peeled, halved, seeded, and sliced
    2 tablespoons plain yogurt
    2 teaspoons honey
    1 teaspoon lemon juice
    1 tablespoon thinly sliced mint leaves
    4 lettuce leaves

Grate 2 teaspoons of orange zest into a medium bowl. With a serrated knife, cut the skin and white pith from the orange. Working over the bowl, cut between the membranes, letting the sections drop into the bowl. Squeeze the juice from the membranes into the bowl.

Add the cucumber, yogurt, honey, lemon juice, and mint leaves to the bowl. Toss to coat well. Refrigerate for at least 20 minutes or up to 3 hours.

To serve, place a lettuce leaf on each of 4 salad plates. Divide the salad among the leaves.

Makes 4 servings

Per serving: 40 calories, 1 g protein, 9 g carbohydrates, 1 g fiber, 0 g fat, 0 g saturated fat, 5 mg sodium

Quinoa Salad with Cherries and Pecans

Quinoa is a high-protein "heirloom" grain with a sweet, nutty flavor and a light texture. This side dish also makes a great breakfast.

1½ cups water
1 cup quinoa, rinsed and drained
½ teaspoon olive oil
1 red onion, chopped
1 tablespoon honey
¼ teaspoon ground cinnamon
2 cups dark, sweet cherries, fresh or frozen and thawed, pitted, and chopped
½ cup pecans, toasted
2 tablespoons chopped parsley

Bring the water to a boil in a medium saucepan. Add the quinoa, cover, and reduce the heat to low. Simmer for 15 minutes, or until the water is absorbed. Uncover and allow to cool.

Heat the oil in a nonstick skillet over medium heat. Add the onion and cook for 5 minutes, or until it begins to brown. Remove from the heat and stir in the honey and cinnamon. Set aside to cool.

In a large bowl, combine the quinoa, onion, cherries, and pecans and toss well. Sprinkle with the parsley.

Makes 4 servings

Per serving: 378 calories, 10 g protein, 57 g carbohydrates, 8 g fiber, 14 g fat, 1 g saturated fat, 5 mg sodium

Monica's Story

When Monica came to see me, she was definite about her goal: "I want you to hypnotize me to lose 25 pounds." As she described her frustration with managing her weight, it seemed as though she was describing another person. Outwardly, she was living an enviable and successful life. At 57, she owned and managed a successful real estate agency. She was married, with a daughter in 12th grade and a son in 10th. Her kids were doing well, and her marriage was stable, if not passionate, after 32 years.

Yet inwardly she was terribly frustrated with herself for failing at this very personal challenge. As her weight had crept up over the past decade, she had felt increasingly ashamed and discouraged. She put on a good face for her employees and customers, but she was depressed. Her many failures with dieting made her ambivalent about trying again. She felt defeated.

Monica was not grossly obese, but she was ashamed of her body. She struggled each morning to find clothes she felt comfortable wearing. Her shame about her appearance made her reluctant to go to the gym. She loved to swim, but she felt too self-conscious to wear a bathing suit.

Although I didn't know what it was, it was clear that something was holding Monica back. "Sorry, Monica; I can't hypnotize you to lose weight. There's a reason you haven't been successful, and you need to understand it and deal with it. Once you do, I can use hypnosis to reinforce your intention to change your eating and exercise habits, and to help you lose weight."

In a guided meditation, I asked Monica to think about what made it so difficult for her to manage her weight. She shared that she had poured herself into her career, which had left little time and energy for her family and even less for herself. She felt guilty for having put her career ahead of her family when her children were small. In recent years, she'd tried to compensate by being more available to her family. In the process, Monica neglected her own basic needs. She ate poorly, didn't exercise, and rarely got enough sleep. Virtually all of her energy went into her business and her family.

In order for Monica to lose weight, she needed to direct some energy into caring for herself. I asked how much her children actually needed her now. She acknowledged that they were both doing well and no longer needed as much attention as they had when they were younger. Both kids were busy with school, extracurricular activities, and their friends. Monica realized it wasn't necessary to neglect herself for her children's sake. She could devote some time to herself while also being available to her children. While this may sound obvious, it hadn't been to Monica. Her lingering guilt had been keeping her from believing it was okay to focus on her own health. Resolving that guilt freed her to invest energy into taking better care of herself. She developed a detailed plan for healthy eating and a practical, sustainable exercise program.

Freed from guilt about caring for herself, Monica was ready to really care for her body. I wove that theme into a hypnotic experience that highlighted her motivation to implement her eating and exercise plan. As I guided her in hypnosis, she eagerly absorbed the empowering images and messages. She felt hopeful about her ability to finally lose weight. She left my office with a recording of the hypnotic experience to listen to at home.

Monica called me 6 months later. She was thrilled to tell me that she had lost the 25 pounds and was no longer depressed. She was taking walks outside every day, eating healthfully, and sleeping well. She was feeling much more comfortable with her body and happier with herself. Her relationship with her family hadn't suffered; in fact, it had gotten better. Her kids and her husband were supportive and proud of her for taking care of herself. They were pleased that she was happier, and they told her so. Feeling better about herself and her body had also helped rekindle the spark in her relationship with her husband.

Many overweight people, like Monica, have depressed, self-critical feelings in relation to their bodies. When they give themselves permission to fully care for themselves, they lose their depressed feelings along with their weight.

Chapter 17

WALK TOWARD A BETTER STATE OF MIND

A journey of a thousand miles begins with a single step.

Lao-tzu

Walking is the most natural physical activity known to human-kind. Although it is simple to do, walking can provide enormous psychological and physical benefits. Walking briskly for as little as 30 minutes three times a week has been shown to significantly enhance mood and increase fitness levels. In this expanded edition of *The Mind-Body Mood Solution,* you will find useful tips and tricks to help you ease into a walking program.

Motivation is the key to starting your walking program. If you are lucky enough to have a friend who will literally pull you out the door, now is the time to ask for that favor. If you are so out of shape that even a 5-minute stroll seems like too much, concentrate on how much better you'll feel afterward, and how that feeling will continue to grow as walking becomes a daily habit.

Don't let things stop you—more importantly, don't let *you* stop you. Use your walking program as a way to solve problems, accomplish goals, regain some control, improvise, and gain strength and resilience. Use it as an analogy for life. Find your inspiration. "Walking opens us up. It feeds us," writes Julia Cameron, author of *The Vein of Gold: A Journey to Your Creative Heart.* "Image by image, it spoons up for us a broth or soup of soul food, which sustains us as we do the work to shape and reshape our lives. . . . Our internal horizons stretch with our external ones. We walk into expanded possibility." Perhaps walking will be that opening into possibility for you.

I've laid out a progressive, 10-week walking program to get you started (see below). In this exclusive edition, you will find additional advice to help you succeed while enjoying every step you take.

WEEK ONE

Find the Right Environment

Whatever the weather, you can find a walking environment that is comfortable and enjoyable for you.

You can go for a walk anytime you want, anywhere you want. That's what makes walking such a great activity: It's so convenient!

But if you're just starting a walking program and you're trying to make it a habit, you need to make a plan. You can't rely on a spur-of-the-moment urge to take a walk, unless you naturally get that urge every day.

Location Makes a Difference

When you're deciding where to walk, try to find a place that is both attractive *and* convenient.

You may know a wonderful trail through a beautiful park

across town. But if driving there takes you 20 minutes, are you willing to make that trip every day or even several days a week? Or perhaps there's a path close to your workplace, but it's littered with trash and so close to traffic that you'd be inhaling exhaust fumes instead of fresh air. Walking in a noisy, toxic environment may actually create more stress than it relieves. And breathing in excessive traffic fumes is harmful to your health. Even if you live in a congested urban area, there are green spaces and walkways along bodies of water that are healthier places to walk.

If you can walk out your front door to a sidewalk that takes you safely around your neighborhood, that's great. But if you live in an area with no sidewalks and or where there are cars coming around blind curves at 50 miles an hour, you are going to have to be creative. Here are some suggestions.

Municipal parks. You may find that the best place to walk is in a nearby municipal park. They usually provide bathroom facilities and water fountains, and many have mileage markers so you can monitor your distance and check your pace. Try to avoid parks where walkers and cyclists share the same paths. Mixed-use trails can be very hazardous, especially for walkers who are talking or wearing headphones and who therefore don't hear cyclists speeding up behind them.

County and state parks. Many have great walking and hiking trails. Call your local parks and recreation department, or go online to get maps. Also, find out whether the trails are considered safe for solitary walkers or if you're better off with a partner. In general, if lots of people use the trails, there's safety in numbers. If a park is all but deserted, think twice before going there alone.

Tracks. High school and college tracks are great when you want to work on your walking technique, when you are trying to improve your speed, or when you just want to get in your miles and go home. If you're on a track for the first time, you may want to see how long it takes you to do a mile—usually four laps—at a comfortable pace. Also, check whether your local YMCA, college, or health club has an indoor track. They are ideal for days when you don't want to walk outside.

Malls. More walkers are taking advantage of the temperature-controlled, traffic-free environment at their local mall. If you walk in a multistory mall, you can use the stairs to improve your endurance and build stronger leg muscles. Many malls open their doors early to walkers who want to get in their workouts before the stores open and shoppers arrive. You can find out whether your local mall has such a policy by calling the administrative office.

Change Course? It's Your Choice

Some walkers prefer to stay on one route. They like to watch the changes from day to day or from season to season. Maybe they look forward to interacting with certain people or animals they meet along the way. Or they appreciate the familiarity of the route because they can relax and let their minds drift, perhaps to mull over problems and come up with solutions.

Other walkers need to change routes to keep themselves stimulated and entertained. They may walk further and longer on weekends, and they constantly look for interesting places to do that. Canal paths, river parks, converted railroads, athletic fields, nature conservancies, and interesting neighborhoods are all good places to walk. For some, the excitement of discovering new paths and wondering what's around the bend makes walking fun. So think about your own likes and interests, and then spend some time finding routes that suit you.

Timing Is Everything

Most experts recommend walking first thing in the morning. By getting it out of the way early, there's less of a chance that your workout will be sidelined by other obligations that arise over the course of a day.

If this works for you, fantastic. You might find that an early-morning walk makes a great start to a productive day. By the time you finish your workout, your energy level may be up, and you might feel relaxed and energized. If you get out the door early enough, you'll beat the early morning commuters. That means there's less traffic and less car exhaust to deal with. However, if you're not a morning person, don't try to force yourself to become one. You need to find a time to walk that suits your schedule and your lifestyle.

For you, lunch may be the perfect time to walk, especially if you work outside your home and you have young children or other responsibilities that keep you from getting out of the house early in the morning or after dinner. For working parents, a lunch-hour workout can seem like a minivacation. It provides a great opportunity for you to de-stress.

One word of advice: Try to walk first and eat lunch afterward. That way, you can travel at a brisk pace without upsetting your digestive system. If you're starving by lunchtime, eat a small snack to tide you over until you're done with your workout.

Music to Keep You Moving

Music can light you up and keep you going, whether you are outside or on a treadmill. The trick is to match your musical preferences to your walking pace.

Composers James and Karen Sundquist, who have worked with the Medical and Sports Music Institute of America, recommend certain music styles that lend themselves to different walking speeds. Here are their suggestions, arranged by beats per minute (BPM).

100 BPM (2 MPH, or a 30-minute mile): classical, bolero, slow waltzes, blues, reggae, rumba, samba, hip-hop.

120 BPM (3 MPH, or a 20-minute mile): march, rock, mainstream pop, disco, soul, ragtime, Broadway show tunes, country, slow fox-trot, tango, big band.

140 BPM (4 MPH, or a 15-minute mile): techno pop, big band, classical, jazz, square dance, polka, Broadway show tunes.

Note: You can also find pacing tapes with music chosen specifically for different types of exercise by visiting the Web site workoutmusicvideo.com.

WEEK TWO

Practice Proper Form

Correct posture appears fluid and effortless. It decreases your chances of suffering an injury and makes walking much easier and more pleasurable. It can even make you feel better! Here's how to align yourself so you move with ease.

Walking really is the simplest form of exercise, but if you are walking regularly, poor posture or technique may lead to pain or injury. On the other hand, correcting those problems allows you to use walking as a wonderful way to rebalance and restore your body's natural symmetry and strength. It can help you stand taller, plant your feet more firmly, and look ahead—literally and figuratively.

Most walkers aren't aware of whether they're walking inefficiently and making it harder on themselves, says Cambridge, Massachusetts–based fitness walking and racewalking coach Ken Mattsson. "Many people jolt and jerk around when they walk, for example," he says. Or they swing their arms out too much. Such offenses might sound minor, but over time, their effects can result in a walking injury.

To keep you stepping out in proper form, here's what Mattsson and other leading walking coaches say about the top two common mistakes walkers make and how to correct them.

Mistake 1: Your posture is poor. "Many walkers get hurt because they simply don't walk erect," says Bonnie Stein, a racewalking coach in Redington Shores, Florida. The two most common posture problems? Walking bent over with your head down, and the opposite: strolling while leaning back. Either way, you set yourself up for injury. Leaning too far forward or backward throws your body off balance, putting undue stress on your lower back, says Stein. The result? Strain and pain.

How to fix it: Stand straight—not rigidly so, but simply tall and relaxed, with your shoulders down and your neck elongated. Your eyes, shoulders, hips, knees, and ankles should all be in line between each stride. Keep your head up and your eyes looking straight ahead, and focus on looking about 15 feet in front of you while keeping your chin parallel to the ground, not tucked in. Keep your shoulders loose and your stomach tucked in a bit, but not so much that you can't breathe freely and deeply. Check yourself in a mirror. Start getting a body sense/memory of what it feels like to stand up straight and walk that way.

Mistake 2: Your style is sloppy. Flapping arms, giant-size strides, stomping feet: These are among the more common "moving violations" walkers make, says Mattsson. These are the types of errors that not only slow you down, but can also set you up for injuries such as shin splints.

How to fix it: Yes, your arms should swing back and forth freely, but they shouldn't flap from side to side or shoot up and take jabs at your chin. Keep your arms mostly bent at about a 90-degree angle. Let them swing close to your torso but not rise above your chest at the pinnacle of the swing. They should drive back, not outward, with each swing.

As for your step, taking too long a stride will actually slow you down, because a heel extended too far in front of your body doesn't generate any forward propulsion. Also, when your foot is stretched out in front of you, it is acting like a brake; you can't easily roll from heel to toe to generate forward power.

Find your proper stride this way: Stand up straight and extend your foot a few inches in front of you so your heel is not quite touching the ground. Start to fall forward slowly; your extended heel will hit the ground and stop you. That's where your front foot should be during your stride, says Stein. Don't focus on where your back leg is during this test. When you're actually walking, your back leg will be farther back.

Pay attention to the sound your feet make as they strike the ground. As you step forward, your heel should strike gently before your foot rolls forward and allows you to push off from your toes. You're stressing your feet and legs needlessly if you come down too hard. You want to move forward, not downward. Let your weight shift naturally from your heel to your toes and push off your toes to propel you into your next step.

If you're walking on a treadmill, it's easy to start pounding rubber. Are your feet going *poom, poom, poom?* If so, you're landing flat-footed. Instead, try landing on your heel, at about a 45-degree angle, and rolling your foot forward. You may have to slow down at first to do this.

Comfortable Shoes Are Key

The correct shoe is essential to helping prevent injury and allowing you to focus on enjoying your walks. If you've ever had a pair of shoes that just didn't feel right, don't despair. There is a shoe out there for just about every foot. Here are some tips for getting the right shoe for you.

- Shop at the end of the day, when your feet are largest.
- Wear your walking socks. Some styles are really thick, and you may need shoes half a size larger to accommodate them.
- Get your feet measured, if possible. Feet tend to flatten out and get bigger as we age, and they also need room to push off as you walk. Lots of people try to squeeze into shoes

that are too small. Make sure there is at least a finger's width of space beyond the end of your longest toe when you are standing up.

- Spend some time in the shoes you are trying on. Walk around the store. If you're in a mall, ask if you can take a few laps around the inside corridors. The shoes should feel great from the start. Don't count on "breaking them in" to make them feel comfortable.

WEEK THREE

Smart Walking Strategies

Here are a dozen ways to stick with the program, even when life gets in the way.

With every skipped walk, you cheat yourself out of a chance to boost your mood and feel better. Surveys confirm that lack of time is the main culprit behind skipping exercising. Here are ways to find more time—and ways to take advantage of the time you already have, but don't realize is there. Before you know it, you'll be lacing up your shoes and heading out for your walk every day!

To boost the odds of always fitting in your walks, do the same things at the same time every day. That includes going to bed, waking up, eating meals, and taking walks. (A regular routine also enhances your sleep, eating, and digestion.) Keeping to this sort of strict schedule isn't always possible, of course, but by attempting to maintain a consistent schedule, you'll make it easier to meet your walking goals.

1. **Make the commitment.** If you really want to walk, you'll find the time. It's not any different from finding time to eat. Think about it: Don't you always have time for that?

Think of walking the same way you think of eating: as a necessity, not an optional activity.

2. **Remember the benefits.** Always keep in mind that by making your walk a high priority a few days a week, you're boosting your own physical and emotional health and lifting your mood.

3. **Ditch the "all-or-nothing" mindset.** Cut back when you need to, but don't stop your workouts altogether because of work deadlines, a sick family member, and so on. Squeeze in a walk of some length—15 minutes, 10 minutes—every second or third day. Then resume your regular routine as soon as you can.

4. **Stop negative thoughts.** Don't buy into the voice in your head that says, "I don't feel like it" or "I should toss in some laundry or organize my closets or pay bills instead of walking." If you allow too many alternatives to edge out your walk, you'll never find time for it.

5. **Go with the flow.** Don't write off your walk every time circumstances change. If a surprise meeting cancels your 30-minute lunchtime stroll, then go after work. If you oversleep, walk at lunch.

6. **Pencil in your walks.** Do this at the start of the week, before the blank spaces in your calendar start filling up with errands and other time thieves. Use your day planner, smartphone, or whatever system you have for scheduling your week's activities.

7. **Use small chunks of time.** If you only have 10 minutes instead of 20, use them. Just do a shorter, brisker walk than you had planned.

8. **Use the stairs.** Find any excuse you can to use the stairs. Don't ask anyone else to run up the stairs for something. Go yourself. Avoid the elevator for a flight or two and take the stairs. Sitting at your desk all day? Take a 2-minute break to go up and down the stairs twice a day.

9. **Divvy it up.** If you need to, break up your daily walking goal into three 10-minute jaunts, six 5-minute spurts, or even fifteen 2-minute quickies. (That last one is roughly equivalent to the number of commercial breaks in an evening spent watching television.)

10. **Seize every opportunity.** Take an extra lap around the perimeter of the grocery store or mall when you're shopping. Catching up on phone calls to friends or family? Pace a little during the conversation. Fido needs to be walked? Don't wait for someone else to volunteer—leash up the dog and head outside. Got mail? Scout out a drop box that's a 10-minute walk away. You get the idea.

11. **Make time with commercials.** You don't have to choose between walking and watching TV. Many would-be walkers who claim they have "no time to exercise" find time to watch TV—Americans watch 23 hours a week, on average. Every hour-long show has about 20 minutes' worth of commercials that you can use as walking time. Instead of watching broadcasts of your favorite shows, record them, watch them without the commercials, and spend that found time walking.

12. **Turn rush hour into walk time.** Walk after work while everyone else is sitting in traffic. By the time you've finished, the whole mess will have cleared out.

WEEK FOUR

Stretch to Relax

Regular stretching is a powerful way to keep your body relaxed and limber. The feeling of relaxation will provide an overall sense of well-being and make your walks more comfortable and enjoyable.

Stretching is just as important as strengthening. And it's especially vital if you find yourself tensing up under stress. Every muscle in your body contains "stretch receptors" that are in constant dialogue with your brain; these receptors convey your overall level of tension. When your muscles are chronically tight, your body is thrown out of alignment, creating muscular imbalances and poor posture. That tells your brain that your body is under stress. When you can deeply relax your body, as you might do during a restorative yoga class or a session of progressive relaxation, you relax your mind, too. The result? A brighter, more open outlook and a restful night's sleep.

The following stretches target the areas that walkers need to pay specific attention to.

Calf and Shin Stretches

WALL STRETCH

Stand an arm's length away from a wall, and place your palms flat against it.

Extend your right leg 2 to 3 feet behind you, and press your right heel to the floor. (Your left knee will bend naturally as you do this.) Keep both heels flat against the floor. Hold for 30 seconds, then return to the starting position. Repeat with your left leg.

STEP STRETCH

Stand facing a step or curb, with your legs hip-width apart and your back straight. Keeping your right foot flat on the ground, step forward with your left foot, resting the ball of your foot on the edge of the step and allowing your heel to lower toward the ground. Slowly lean forward until you feel a stretch in your calf. Hold for 30 seconds, then return to the starting position. Repeat with your right leg.

Hamstrings

LEG EXTENSION AND PULL

Lie on the floor with your knees bent and your back flat. (You'll be more comfortable if you do this one on a carpeted or well-padded surface.)

Keeping both hips on the floor, slowly straighten your right knee and lift your right leg straight toward the ceiling with your foot flexed. Grasp your thigh just above your knee, and pull gently to increase the stretch. Hold for 30 seconds, then return to the starting position. Repeat with your left leg.

To make this stretch more difficult, begin with both legs fully extended on the floor. Then bend your right knee up toward your chest, and slowly straighten it toward the ceiling with your foot flexed. Hold and repeat, as instructed above.

Hips

STAIR STRETCH

Stand facing away from a low chair or the bottom of a staircase. Carefully extend your right leg behind you, placing the top of your foot on the seat of the chair or one of the lower steps behind you. Place your hands on your hips, or hold on to a table or wall for support.

Keeping your right foot securely in place, gently pull your right thigh forward so that you feel a mild pulling through your right hip and thigh. Hold, then return to the starting position. Repeat with your left leg.

CROSSOVER LEG PULL

Lie on your back with your right leg bent at about a 90-degree angle and your right foot flat on the floor. Bend your left leg and cross your left ankle over your right knee.

Clasp your hands behind your right knee, and gently pull your right leg up and toward you, keeping your left leg open and your left knee out to the side. When you feel the stretch in your hip and inner thigh, stop and hold for 30 seconds, then return to the starting position. Repeat with your left leg.

Shoulders

OVERHEAD REACH

Stand with your feet shoulder-width apart, your head in line with your spine, your back straight, and your eyes facing forward.

Maintain that position as you slowly and gently raise both arms in front of you until directly over your head. Be careful not to arch your back. When your arms are directly overhead, lace your fingers together with your palms facing the ceiling. Hold, then return to the starting position.

PRAISE POSE

Get down on your hands and knees, with your back flat, your neck straight, and your eyes facing toward the floor.

Slowly shift your weight back until your butt rests on your heels and your arms are straight out in front of you. Try to keep your hands in their original position: Do not allow them to shift back as you bend. You should feel a stretch in your arms, shoulders, and hips.

Arms

BACK SCRATCH STRETCH

Stand with your feet shoulder-width apart, your back straight, your head in line with your spine, and your eyes facing forward. Raise your left arm over your head, bend your elbow, and reach your hand down behind your head to the middle of your back. The fingers of your left hand should fall between your shoulder blades, and your left elbow should point toward the ceiling.

Keeping your shoulders down, grasp your left elbow with your right hand and gently push your elbow down until you feel the stretch in the back of your arm. Hold, then return to the starting position. Repeat with your right arm.

OPEN ARMS

Stand with your feet shoulder-width apart and your knees slightly bent. Keep your back straight and your head up.

Slowly raise your arms up and out to your sides until they reach shoulder level. With your palms facing forward, gently reach your arms back behind you. When you have reached back as far as is comfortably possible, bend your wrists back until you feel a stretch in the fronts of your upper arms. Hold, then slowly return to the starting position.

Quadriceps

STORK STRETCH

Stand with your left hand resting on a chair or a table for support. Bend your right leg behind you and grasp the top of your right foot with your right hand, keeping your back straight and your eyes and hips forward.

Slowly pull the heel of your foot toward your butt (don't pull it all the way up or you risk injuring your leg), stopping when you feel tension in your quadriceps. Be sure to keep your hips and knees aligned with one another. Do not lock the knee of your standing leg. Hold, then return to the starting position. Repeat with your left leg.

WEEK FIVE

Pair Up for Success

Sometimes, a walking buddy can be the best thing since new sneakers. Here's how to cultivate this special relationship.

To reap all of the physical and mental benefits of walking, you need to do it every day—or almost every day—for the rest of your life. That's a tall order, even for a dedicated walker. You'll have days when you are short on time, energy, or motivation, and you need a little extra nudge to put on your walking shoes. Of course, once you are out walking, you'll feel great.

Even if you enjoy the solitude of walking, sometimes you may need a buddy to keep you going. Teaming up with a partner can keep your motivation from slipping and your walking program on track, even when you're convinced that you have other "more important" things to do.

Of course, you can undertake a walking program on your own.

But studies show that people are more likely to stick with fitness routines of all kinds if they have a partner. We humans need social support.

Anyone can become your walking partner: a family member, a friend, a co-worker, a neighbor, or even a dog. If you can't find one person who's willing to walk with you every day, recruit two or three people, each of whom can keep you company at various times throughout the week.

To maintain your motivation, you and your most frequent walking partner should share a similar agenda. Maybe both of you want to improve your fitness levels or work off stress. Or maybe you enjoy bird-watching or window-shopping while you walk. Whatever your mutual goals or pleasures, they'll keep the two of you coming together for regular, consistent walks.

Stepping Out with Your Spouse

When you're looking for a walking partner, you may want to start your search close to home. That way, each time you exercise, you have an opportunity to strengthen the relationships that contribute most to your sense of happiness and well-being.

If you're married, you may want to ask your spouse to walk with you. Walking together can be a fun, romantic interlude. Away from household duties and distractions, you may feel a sense of freedom to simply enjoy being together. The invigorating physical activity and mood-enhancing effects of sunshine and the natural world also help you to bring out the best in each other. And when you're both in a positive frame of mind, you'll be better able to address any issues that you and your spouse might want to discuss.

In fact, many couples say that it's easier to communicate with each other when they're walking. They're more comfortable opening up to each other because they're side-by-side rather than face-to-face. And because walking can release tension, they're more likely to feel calm while discussing sensitive or divisive issues.

Connecting with Kids

Kids can be great walking partners, provided you choose a destination that's of interest to them. Suggest going for a walk to a friend's house, an ice cream parlor, a playground, or a park. Most children will gladly go the distance if the end goal is enticing enough. With older kids, you'll be able to walk at your exercise pace. With small children, you won't get aerobic exercise, but you'll both have fun · strolling at their pace.

Walking on the Job

Outside of your family, you may be able to find a walking partner or two among your co-workers. Everyone gets breaks, and using that time to walk can do more to de-stress and re-energize you than coffee and a doughnut ever will.

Try to block out part of your lunch hour for walking, too. You don't want to skip lunch completely, but save 10 to 15 minutes for a walk. It can be a great stress reliever. Keep an extra pair of walking shoes and socks at work, so you can be ready at a moment's notice. For really brisk walks on warm days, you may want to change into workout clothes.

Partner with a Pooch

When you're considering a walking partner, don't overlook the four-legged variety. Walking with a dog isn't for everyone, and I certainly don't advise adopting a dog just for your walking program. But a pooch can be a most devoted and reliable walking partner. The great thing about dogs is that they always want to go for a walk. They even remind you when it's time to go.

If you want to walk a dog but aren't ready to commit to a long-term relationship, plenty of animal shelters welcome volunteer dog-walkers. Or you can ask to take a friend's dog for a walk.

WEEK SIX

Reconnect to the Natural World

Finding new places outdoors can help you reconnect with nature and more deeply connect with yourself. The next new place could be right in your neighborhood. Be inspired to become an explorer.

Have you ever taken a walk and had so much going on in your mind that you hardly noticed, much less appreciated, what was going on around you? I have. I've walked through a beautiful landscape so lost in my thoughts and disconnected from my surroundings that I've arrived home almost unaware of where I'd been. Nature can be profoundly nourishing, but only if we are present to it. The exercises below can help you fine-tune your ability to experience the richness of the natural world.

Exercises for the Senses

The exercises below are intended to awaken or sharpen your senses. By using these senses to explore the natural world on a deeper level, you come to realize that you're a part of nature, not apart from it. Keep in mind that there are no right or wrong results. Just enjoy yourself!

Explore without your eyes. In some safe spot outside, close your eyes and stand quietly. Become aware of the input you're receiving from your other senses now that your dominant sense, vision, is "turned off." Pay attention to your sense of balance, the ground underfoot, and your sense of direction based on the sun or the wind. Notice whether you can feel the presence of trees or rocks around you without touching them. Occasionally open your eyes for a second and notice how your environment looks. Many people report a heightened awareness of color and shape after this exercise.

See with your hands. Before you begin to walk, go outside and pick up five or six pebbles of similar shape and size. Mark one with a felt-tip marker. Put the rest in your pocket. Hold the marked stone in your hand as you walk, learning to recognize it by touch. After 5 or 10 minutes, drop the stone into your pocket with the others and mix them up. Then, without looking in your pocket, reach in and see if you can pick out the marked stone. Repeat the activity with new stones, or just mark a different stone. You'll find that every stone really feels different, even when they look similar.

Connect with your breath. This exercise reminds us that we humans are part of the web of life on planet Earth. It's just as the 19th-century American naturalist John Muir once said: "When we try to pick out anything by itself, we find it hitched to everything else in the universe."

For this exercise, all you do is think about breathing. Remember that plants release the oxygen that you breathe into your lungs; in return, you breathe out the carbon dioxide that plants take in.

In your mind's eye, follow your breath as you exhale. Imagine that you can see the carbon dioxide molecules leaving your nose or mouth and flowing into the leaves on the plants nearest you as you walk. At the same time, envision yourself inhaling the oxygen that the plants give off. Take a moment to note how your visualization of this very natural process affects your sense of the world around you.

Acknowledge your appreciation. Think of the wonderful feeling you get when you say "thank you" to someone who has given you a gift or compliment. When you see a beautiful tree and you stop for a moment to experience your appreciation of its beauty, you're sending a mental thank-you to that tree. Try this exercise and notice how it affects your perception of the world around you.

First, suspend any preconceived notions of what's pleasing or attractive and just observe your enviroment. You may find yourself drawn to a certain color, a particular smell, a certain view, or something else. As you become aware of the object or the environment, take a moment to appreciate that it has made you feel good. Mentally thank whatever has attracted you.

If you'd like to explore more of these types of exercises, you can find them in the book *Reconnecting with Nature*, by Michael J. Cohen. These activities can help transform your walks into moving meditations that calm, refresh, and revitalize you. They will help you connect deeply with nature, and in so doing, connect more deeply with yourself.

WEEK SEVEN

Unlock Your Creativity

Whether you're in your office or outdoors, you can use walks to think about problems, find solutions, and just break out of the box.

Ever notice that your thinking has gotten stuck in an unproductive loop? Whether you want to be more creative; find new, better ways of doing things; or get a fresh perspective on tough problems, my advice is the same: Take a walk!

Research has shown that walking can enhance creativity. In one study, all 63 participants showed a significant increase in the flow of creative ideas after just 25 minutes of aerobic activity. Exercise induces a relaxed mental state that allows thinking to be more complex, expansive, and creative than when we are tense. Tension and stress block the flow of creative ideas, so when we are more relaxed, our thinking is more creative than when we are tense. Exercise induces our brains to enter a state of relaxation. Thoughts that, in a more uptight mental state, would be kept in separate compartments are, in this looser mindset, juggled together. The results are a delicious stew of new ideas.

Walking to Create

For many people in creative professions, walking is a direct path to doing better work. While you're taking a break from the actual process, part of your brain is working on ideas, formats, and connections. You come back to your desk, easel, or computer screen with a fresher mind and new ideas to try out. You may even want to take a little notepad and pen along with you to write down the good ideas you have as you walk, so you don't forget them! For creative walking, it helps if you can slip easily away from schedules and structure and allow your mind to be free.

Walking to Solve Problems

Many people report that one of the most valuable benefits of walking is discovering a resolution to a personal or professional challenge. Answers may not come instantly, but over time, you may go from worrying about something to coming up with solutions. Like "sleeping" on a problem, your mind seems to work on problems while you're walking, even if you're not consciously aware of it. Next time you're at an impasse, try heading out the door and see what happens.

Walking Outdoors

When we're walking in the great outdoors, our minds are free to run through an unexplored wilderness of ideas. Wilderness—quite literally—and other varieties of nature may be key factors in the trek to creativity.

"Walking outdoors reminds us of who we are," says James A. Swan, PhD, author of *Nature as Teacher and Healer* and an environmental psychologist in Mill Valley, California. "Studies have shown that spending as little as an hour a week in a natural area can have a positive influence on creativity."

Taking a stroll outside is particularly meaningful in today's "information age," Dr. Swan says. "We've come to rely on the printed page or television to tell us which way the wind is blowing and have become divorced from ourselves," he says. "When you walk in nature, your mind will naturally sink back into a place where you recognize your own past experiences and come to know your own feelings."

Walking in nature can also give you a healthy perspective. You can sense the immensity of the universe and move beyond the narrow confines of your immediate home and work life. This expanded perspective can be profoundly nourishing and uplifting.

WEEK EIGHT

Boost the Burn

Ready to add some fat-blasting days to your walks? Here's how: with walking poles, interval walking, and a hill or two.

Once you've mastered a basic walking program, you may want to take it up a notch to further improve your fitness. You can do that by going a bit faster, using a more powerful stride, walking for longer times and distances, and tackling hills to spike your aerobic capacity and fat-burning potential.

Interval Walking

This is a good way to increase your fitness level without spending more time exercising. It involves alternating short bursts of strenuous exercise with lower-intensity recovery periods. It lets you exercise longer at a higher intensity by breaking up the high-intensity periods into short segments. And, over time, the higher-intensity exercise builds more muscle and helps you burn fat better. It's best to have been walking consistently for at least 6 weeks before starting interval training.

There are no set-in-stone rules about how to do interval training.

The general idea is that, after you've warmed up, you intermittently push yourself hard for short bursts of activity. One good way to do this is to use landmarks as goals. For example, walk as fast as you can to a stop sign up ahead. Then give yourself plenty of time to recover, walking more slowly, before you start another speed interval. You've recovered when you are back to breathing a little harder than normal. Do three to five 20- to 30-second intervals, during each walk for at least 4 or 5 weeks. Do it only every other day, at first. Eventually, you may work up to about 20 minutes of 1:1 interval training. (That's one minute of high-intensity exercise followed by one minute of lower-intensity recovery exercise, for 20 minutes total.) Don't forget to warm up for 10 to 15 minutes and to cool down for the same amount of time.

Pole Walking

You've probably seen people using walking poles. They look like ski poles, but have rubber tips. Poles are great for people who need to stabilize themselves on uneven terrain or who need to take some impact off their legs. They're quite useful for people who are overweight or who have some osteoarthritis in their knees, hips, or feet. They help you walk longer, with less pain, but they also do more than that!

Like swimming or cross-country skiing, pole walking is a whole-body workout. It works your core body muscles, including your abdominals and the long muscles that run along your spine. One study found a 40 percent increase in muscle endurance—the ability to do work for a longer period of time—for pole walkers. And this was with *no* increased sense of exertion! If you *do* put some effort into it by extending your arms further and pushing down on your poles as you walk, you can boost your calorie burn by 50 to 70 percent, says Tom Rutlin, one of the best-known walking pole advocates in the United States. "The more force you apply to the poles, the more calories you burn," he says. "It's like working against resistance on a weight machine." And it builds muscle the same way.

If you decide to buy walking poles, expect to pay between $70 and $100 for a nice pair. Features to look for include a cushy, ergonomic grip, adjustable height, and interchangeable tips (rubber and ice spike).

Hills and Inclines

If you've ever used a treadmill, you know how every degree of incline pushes up the calorie burn—and the effort you must make to achieve it. But think of hills as your friends. They can help make you stronger and increase your endurance. Start slowly, and slow down if you feel any discomfort. Start out with a gradual slope, if you can. If a steep grade is all you have, stop as often as you need to in order to catch your breath. Expect to feel some muscle soreness, particularly in the front of your legs and your Achilles tendon at the back of your ankle, after your first few times hill walking.

If the hills in your area are anthills, consider stair climbing to boost your walking workouts. Stairs are the equivalent of a 50 percent incline, so go slowly at first and stretch out your calves afterward.

WEEK NINE

Heal Your Spirit

Awareness and conscious breathing can bring a sense of wholeness and appreciation to the world unfolding around you.

Walking may be good for the body, but it also provides food for the spirit. Walking in beautiful, natural surroundings has a special regenerative power for the spirit. Sometimes you'll want to pay close attention, to be "in the now" and less in your head with your thoughts. And when you pay attention, you'll find that traipsing through the woods has a distinctly different flavor than walking on open roads with long-distance vistas. They're two wonderful and distinct pleasures.

In the woods, you can feel an intimacy with the rocks, the trees, the leaves, and the smell of damp earth. You can touch things with your hands and feel the textures under your feet. Since your view is limited, you concentrate on what's nearby.

You usually have to keep an eye on your feet, too, so don't walk too fast. Take time to look around. When you slow down, you see so much more—like the tiny wildflowers that barely catch your eye unless you actually stop to look for them. If you carry a small magnifying glass, those tiny wildflowers will reveal intricate patterns, symmetry, and color.

On an open country road, a hilltop, or in another open space, you can get a sense of expansiveness and exhilaration. You can see great distances and instinctively feel a part of all that space and immense beauty. If you open yourself to it, the sense of sheer power and beauty may flood over you. Joseph Campbell, coauthor of *The Power of Myth,* describes this experience by quoting an ancient Hindu scripture: "When before the beauty of a sunset or of a mountain, you pause and exclaim 'Ah,' you are participating in divinity."

Along with all of the physical benefits to your body and mind, you bring this special healing power of nature to your soul. You don't have to travel to exotic places to do it. Find a beautiful park or neighborhood with a view, or scope out a local trail, and take a slow, leisurely walk. The natural rhythm of walking will relax you and the healing power of natural beauty will refresh you.

Breathe Away Tension

And now I see with eye serene
The very pulse of the machine.
A Being breathing thoughtful breath,
A Traveler between life and death.

—*William Wordsworth*

In any environment, you can focus your attention on your breath as a form of meditation, awareness building, and relaxation. When we are under stress, our breathing tends to become constricted. Breathing in rhythm with our steps is a great way to deeply relax the body and mind. Try the following simple exercise.

Exhale fully, pause, then, as you walk, inhale for four steps. Fill your lungs from bottom to top, breathing air into your belly, rib cage, and up to your collarbone. Then exhale for four steps, expelling air from your upper chest down to your belly until your navel pushes back toward your spine. Segment the breath by pausing slightly, then continuing to inhale or exhale. Do this for about 3 minutes, matching your breaths to your steps. If any feelings come up, breathe through them. Let them go with each exhalation. Then stop for about 5 minutes, but continue walking. Notice any changes in the way you feel or what you see. After about 5 minutes, start again. Repeat two or three more times, and you'll have walked for about half an hour.

WEEK TEN

Keep Walking Fun

If you do the same thing day after day, you'll get bored. Here are some ways to keep motivating yourself and reinventing your walk.

By now you are probably walking dutifully. Doggedly. Occasionally even delightedly. With a little bit of attention, you can bring more delight to your walking. By rearranging some elements of your routine, you can end up with something that's more creative and motivating—in short, more fun. Here are five suggestions—some physical, some mental—that will help you do exactly that.

1. **Be a swinger.** If fun is where the fun people are, head for their hangout: the playground. Just map out a 1½- to 2-mile

route between your house and the nearest elementary school or public playground. Between striding there and back, you'll squeeze in a quick 3- to 4-miler. Plus, you can swing on the monkey bars at the halfway point to get a muscle-building workout. You can even swing on the swings and get a gravity-defying lift.

2. **Field a team.** If one walking partner is an excellent motivator, what are 10 walking partners? They're a team, and a powerful incentive to get in a workout and make it count. Put up signs at work, join a mall-walkers group, or look for people who are in training for a walk-a-thon.

3. **Play with your watch.** Use your watch as a training partner, and beat the tedium of an evenly paced walk even as you improve the quality of your workout. Set your watch to beep every minute or so, and then, at each beep, pick up your pace for about 10 seconds. These shorter bursts can get your body accustomed to a faster speed without wearing you out. In fact, short bursts of exertion can even be energizing and mood elevating.

4. **Feed your senses.** Instead of focusing on creaking knees or sore feet, try shifting your focus to your sense of smell or sight, suggests Diane Ackerman, author of the book *Deep Play*. According to Ackerman, "deep play" is a state in which you're so absorbed in what you're doing that you're alive simply through your senses. "It's a way to break free of some of the rigors and stresses of everyday life," she explains. "As humans, we're afflicted with ourselves most of the time, and it's a wonderful thing if we can get out of ourselves and have a love affair with the world—if we can leave the ordinary behind and enter an extraordinary realm where we feel fully alive."

To reshape your walks as a form of deep play, Ackerman suggests focusing on one particular sense, such as smell or touch, as you stride. You might concentrate only on the bottoms of your feet, exploring what it feels like to move over the Earth. Or focus only on the scents you breathe in as you work your legs and lungs. If you do this, she promises, you will be "present" in your workouts and not struggling with your various stresses.

5. **Don't let your goals defeat you.** A crucial element in maintaining your motivation and enjoyment is how you define success. If your goals are realistically attainable and within your control, they will help to energize you. If they are unreachable, they will frustrate you. If your goal is to walk 9 miles in an hour or lose 5 pounds in a week, you're likely to be sadly disappointed. In general, your behaviors (such as walking a certain number of minutes a week at a certain realistic pace) are more under your control than the consequences of those behaviors (such as weight loss).

Another key to being successful with your walking and your mood is to be kind to yourself. If you have been taking care of a sick family member all week and you haven't been able to do all of your scheduled walking, be gentle with yourself about that. Forgive yourself and then recommit to your goals.

Finally, it is important to realize that success is not only measured in steps, miles, or minutes. Success may also be reflected in feeling the joy of movement, the camaraderie of walking with a friend, or the replenishment of a sound night's sleep. Yes, walking is exercise, but it's much more than that. It can be a time for meditation, inspiration, creativity, friendship, and communion. Connecting with your passion for walking will energize your step and lift your spirits.

Walking the Labyrinth: A Path to Inner Peace

One of the most extraordinary paths you can walk is one that takes you through a labyrinth. The classic labyrinth is a circular path that slowly takes you around and around until you reach the center of the circle, and then takes you back out. Labyrinths are often found near churches and sacred sites, and they serve as a metaphor for the spiritual journey through life. Throughout history, human beings around the world have created and walked labyrinths for personal healing, spiritual transformation, and answers to important life questions. The journey through the labyrinth expresses the universal striving toward wholeness, connection with the Earth, and alignment with the divine.

Though similar to a maze, a labyrinth is different in one important respect: While a maze has numerous blind alleys and dead ends, a labyrinth is one continuous path that winds its way to the center and back out again. It simply involves walking and trusting that there is a path that takes you exactly where you need to go. All that is required is that you persist in your journey. I hope you have an opportunity sometime soon to walk a labyrinth, and that you continue to find the strength and enthusiasm to persevere in your journey.

Susan's Story

Susan came to me for help with weight loss and depression. At 49, she felt "ugly, old, and fat." She was at her heaviest weight (190 pounds), and at only 5 feet 4 inches tall, was feeling horrible about it. Though she'd been successful with a popular weight-loss program in the past, Susan was finding it very difficult to lose weight now. Feeling ashamed of her appearance, she avoided leaving her house, and her life became constricted. She felt "invisible," which was a source of profound sadness.

She and her husband and their three teenage children had moved a lot because of her husband's job. Susan had left her stimulating job as a marketing manager when she had her first child. The frequent moves around the country made it hard for her to feel grounded and settled, and she lived with a constant feeling of uncertainty. She missed the sense of self-determination, accomplishment, and control she had experienced when she was employed.

I worked with Susan to develop her self-care plan, which included strategies for eating and exercise. Feeling out of control in other parts of her life, she appreciated the structure and accountability that we built into her plan. She welcomed the process of tracking her food and physical activity in her journal. I guided Susan in a visualization in which she imagined herself engaging in healthy eating and exercise and feeling her deep desire to continue these activities. I made a CD of the visualization, and she listened to it often over the next several weeks.

Susan also worked on the obstacles that had made it hard for her to really care for herself. Most significantly, she was consumed with taking care of others. Tearfully she related, "I struggle to keep everybody afloat." Her caretaking had sad, deep roots. When Susan was 15, her mother died. On her deathbed, she beseeched Susan to take care of her father and younger sister. She shouldered the mantle of caretaking responsibility with quiet resignation. She fought back her grief in order to deal with the demands of her day-to day-world.

We did some inner work with the part of her that felt unworthy, invisible, and depressed. She went back in time to adolescence and connected with the sadness that lay beneath her strong sense of responsibility. She realized that her poor self-care and sense of invisibility had to do with trying to hide her sadness. She also saw how covering up her sadness had suppressed her potential for happiness. Allowing herself to feel her sadness connected her with a rich source of emotional vitality. She no longer needed to make her feelings, and herself, invisible. She could finally acknowledge her need to genuinely care for herself. And she realized that she could continue taking care of her family without sacrificing her own well-being.

Before starting her exercise plan, Susan was evaluated by an exercise physiologist. Although she was obese, she was actually fairly fit. During her stay at Canyon Ranch, she played racquetball, swam, walked, and began weight training. At the end of the week, she felt energized and enthusiastic. She planned to continue her physical activities, and she was excited that two of her friends at home were willing to walk and work out with her. She was also looking forward to playing golf with her husband. Susan had been athletic as a child, and she was thrilled to reconnect with that playful, athletic part of herself.

Susan's stay had been cathartic, with the release of many tears and self-imposed limitations. She left Canyon Ranch feeling lighter and much more energetic. She was cautiously optimistic, knowing that she had a long road ahead.

I stayed in touch with Susan by phone. After 8 months she had lost 36 pounds and was delighted with her accomplishment and with herself. She was no longer depressed, and she felt determined and optimistic about continuing her self-care and weight loss.

APPENDIX A

The chart on page 14 gives an overview of supplements that support brain function and cognitive health. The expanded list below goes into greater detail, explaining the function, effects, dosage, and

Complementary Supplement Chart

SUPPLEMENT	FUNCTION	
GABA (gamma-aminobutyric acid)	Fatty acid that functions as inhibitory neurotransmitter	
5-HTP (5-hydroxy-tryptophan)	Amino acid that is converted into serotonin	
L-Theanine	Amino acid that enhances GABA activity and regulates excretion of serotonin, dopamine, epinephrine, and norepinephrine	
Omega-3 (omega-3 fatty acid)	Fatty acid that fortifies cell membranes, enhancing nerve transmission. Improves metabolism, regulates immune system.	
SAMe (s-adenosylmethionine)	Amino acid intermediate that promotes methylation. Boosts production of dopamine, serotonin, and norepinephrine.	
St. John's Wort (Hypericin)	Plant derivative that contains phytonutrients that increase serotonin levels	

interactions of each supplement. As always, consult your physician, nutritionist, naturopath, or psychiatrist with nutritional training before adding any supplements to your diet.

EFFECTS	DOSAGE	TAKE WITH
Promotes calmness; promotes sleep	500 mg once in midafternoon and once before bed	Inositol, niacinimide, vitamins B$_6$ and C, L-Theanine
Promotes calmness; promotes sleep	Start at 50 mg twice a day; increase to a maximum of 150 mg twice a day	Do not take if you are taking tryptophan or a selective serotonin re-uptake inhibitor
Relaxation; helps induce sleep; enhances feelings of well-being and pleasure	200 mg once in the morning and once before bed	5-HTP, GABA
Enhances feelings of calmness, well-being, and alertness	1,000 mg fish oil (with EPA/DHA ratio of 300/200) once in the morning and once in the evening	————————
Promotes energy and well-being; relieves joint pain	Start at 400 mg four times a day or 800 mg twice a day	B-complex; magnesium
Promotes calmness and improves sleep	300 to 450 mg twice a day	Do not take with any other antidepressant or psychotropic medication

(continued)

SUPPLEMENT	FUNCTION	
B Vitamins	Family of vitamins that promotes methylation	
Vitamin D$_3$	A hormone that regulates hundreds of genes that influence most organs in the body; it also functions as an anti-inflammatory	
L-Tyrosine	Amino acid that supports dopamine production	
Magnesium	Mineral responsible for more than 300 enzyme reactions. Helps cells make energy and muscles relax.	
Melatonin	Hormone released by pineal gland during periods of darkness	
Tryptophan	Amino acid that is converted into serotonin	

EFFECTS	DOSAGE	TAKE WITH
Promotes feeling of well-being and enhances cognitive function	Take either 800 mcg of folate; 50–100 mg of B_6 or pyrodixine, or 1,000 mcg of B_{12}	_____
Increases energy and feeling of well-being	2,000 IU daily for maintenance; if deficient, take 5,000 to 10,000 IU daily until Vitamin D level is normal	_____
Enhances energy, alertness, and well-being	Start at 500 mg once before breakfast, once midmorning and once midafternoon. After 3 days, increase to 1,000 mg.	_____
Promotes relaxation; relieves aches, pains, irritability; promotes sleep	400 to 600 mg daily of magnesium citrate or magnesium glycinate. To promote sleep, increase dosage by 200–400 mg	_____
Promotes sleep	1–3 mg before bed. Take only if sleep difficulties persist after taking other relaxing, sleep–promoting supplements.	_____
Promotes relaxation and sleep	500 mg once in the afternoon and once before bed	Do not take if you are taking 5-HTP or a selective serotonin re-uptake inhibitor

APPENDIX B

Using this form to record your activities, feelings, and realizations will help you monitor your progress from day to day. Start by making copies of this form, and keep them where they're readily available

DAILY CHECK-IN

AREA	WHAT YOU DID	HOW YOU FELT
Nutrition		
Exercise		
Sleep		
Breathing		
Presence		
Judgment		
Forgiveness		
Gratitude		
Action		

to record your progress. Then, when you go back to review your answers after a number of days or weeks, you will be able to spot patterns and get a sense of which tools are helping you most.

WHAT YOU REALIZED

EPILOGUE: WAKING UP

Depression is a wake-up call that comes from deep inside you, bearing a message: Something in your life needs to change. By responding to the call of depression, you have chosen to discover what needs to change. By using the tools outlined in this book, you are awakening to the possibility of living a full, vital life. Waking up may be difficult at first, but eventually it brings a renewed sense of energy and freedom to your life.

Waking up reminds me of a story that happened on an early spring day 16 years ago. My son, who was 3 years old at the time, noticed a bright green shoot poking its way through a thin layer of snow by our front steps. Crouching next to it, he said in an excited yet hushed voice, "What's this?"

"Let's see," answered my wife as she knelt down next to him. "It's a daffodil, our first spring flower."

"A daffodil," my son echoed. Then, looking up at me with his eyes filled with wonder, he asked, "How did it get here?"

"Well," I said, "It woke up out of a big seed called a bulb that's been sleeping underground all winter."

My son looked closely at the jagged crack in the half-frozen ground where the daffodil sprout had broken through. "Does it hurt?" he asked. "Does it hurt to wake up?"

"Oh, no, not really," my wife assured him. "When it feels the ground around it warming up, it can't wait to rise up into the sunshine."

He touched the yellow-green sprout. Then he stood up. He turned his face toward the sky, squeezed his eyes closed, clenched his fists, and breathed in a huge gulp of air.

"What are you doing?" my wife asked.

"Sh-h-h-h," he sputtered, letting his breath go. "I'm waking up!"

When we are children, there is a natural momentum to waking up. It's an unfolding part of human development, just like adult teeth coming in and the hormonal changes of puberty. It's inherent in our nature, just as it is for the daffodil. But when you are an adult, waking up requires something more of you. You need to become aware of what your body, mind, and spirit need to heal and thrive. Then, it takes a deliberate act of will to change old patterns and embrace new ones. Openheartedly welcoming a small change—as simple as how you draw in your breath—can profoundly change your mood and your life. Embracing the changes in this book will help you awaken to the possibilities of your life. Make your action plan. Build something beautiful. Then, open the door and go outside. The world is waiting for you.

RESOURCES

In addition to relying on word-of-mouth referrals and recommendations, you can find health care practitioners through professional organizations and Web sites. The following organizations and offer listings of accredited practitioners.

Psychologists

American Psychological Association
The APA maintains a geographical listing of licensed psychologists. Psychologists have a doctoral degree in psychology or education. They have between 5 and 7 years of course work and supervised clinical experience providing psychological testing and psychotherapy.
Phone: 800-374-2721
Web site: apa.org

National Directory of Psychologists
This online directory contains contact information listed by state for psychologists throughout the United States.
E-mail: info@psychologyinfo.com
Web site: psychologyinfo.com

Find-a-Therapist.com
This Web site offers a directory of psychologists as well as a listing of psychologists, psychiatrists, social workers, therapists, and counselors who provide psychotherapy for depression.
Phone: 866-450-3463

Psychiatrists

American Psychiatric Association
This organization is the largest professional organization of psychiatrists in the United States. Psychiatrists are MDs or DOs (doctors of osteopathy) who have completed a 4-year residency in psychiatry. They are qualified to prescribe medication, order laboratory tests, and provide psychotherapy.
Phone: 888-357-7924
E-mail: apa@psych.org
Web site: psych.org

American Psychiatric Nurses Association
Members of this professional organization have training in mental health nursing and are qualified to provide psychotherapy.
Phone: 866-243-2443
Web site: apna.org

Social Workers

National Association of Social Workers
Licensed independent social workers have engaged in 2 years of course

work and supervised training, as well as 1 year of postgraduate supervised clinical experience.
Phone: 202-408-8600
E-mail: credentialing@naswdc.org
Web site: socialworkers.org

Counselors

American Mental Health Counselors Association
This organization represents mental health counselors and maintains a directory of psychotherapists.
Phone: 800-326-2642
Web site: amhca.org

Specific Types of Therapy

Marriage and Family Therapy

American Association for Marriage and Family Therapy
Phone: 703-838-9808
Web site: aamft.org

American Group Psychotherapy Association
Phone: 877-668-2472
E-mail: info@agpa.org
Web site: agpa.org

Association for Contextual Behavioral Science
Web site: contextualpsychology.org

Mind-Body Medicine and Mindfulness

Center for Mindfulness in Medicine, Health Care, and Society
Phone: 508-856-2656
E-mail: mindfulness@umassmed.edu
Web site: umassmed.edu/cfm/index.aspx

The Center for Mind-Body Medicine
Phone: 202-966-7338

E-mail: center@cmbm.org
Web site: cmbm.org

Biofeedback Certification International Alliance
Phone: 866-908-8713
E-mail: info@bcia.org
Web site: bcia.org

Complementary Medicine

Institute for Functional Medicine
Phone: 800-228-0622
E-mail: client_services@fxmed.com
Web site: functionalmedicine.org

American Holistic Medical Association
Phone: 216-292-6644
E-mail: info@holisticmedicine.org
Web site: holisticmedicine.org

American Holistic Nurses Association
Phone: 800-278-2462
E-mail: info@ahna.org
Web site: ahna.org

American College for Advancement in Medicine
Phone: 800-532-3688
Web site: www.acamnet.org

International Society for Orthomolecular Medicine
Phone: 416-733-2117
E-mail: centre@orthomed.org
Web site: orthomed.org

Orthomolecular.org
Phone: 316-682-3100
E-mail: support@orthomolecular.org
Web site: orthomolecular.org

American Association of Naturopathic Physicians
Phone: 866-538-2267
E-mail: member.services@naturopathic.org
Web site: naturopathic.org

Traditional Western Medicine

American Medical Association
Phone: 800-621-8335
Web site: ama-assn.org

American Osteopathic Association
Phone: 800-621-1773
E-mail: info@osteotech.org
Web site: osteopathic.org

Nutrition

American Dietetic Association
Phone: 800-877-1600
E-mail: findnrd@eatright.org
Web site: eatright.org

American Association of Nutritional Consultants
Phone: 888-828-2262
E-mail: registrar@aanc.net
Web site: aanc.net

National Association of Nutrition Professionals
Phone: 800-342-8037
Web site: nanp.org

Exercise

National Academy of Sports Medicine
Phone: 800-460-6276
Web site: nasm.org

Meditation and Retreat Centers

Insight Meditation Society
Phone: 978-355-4378
E-mail: rc@dharma.org
Web site: dharma.org

Independent Meditation Center Guide
Web site: gosit.org

Vipassana Meditation
Web site: dhamma.org

Shambala
Phone: 661-268-0380
E-mail: info@shambala.org
Web site: shambala.org

The Transcendental Meditation Program
Phone: 888-532-7686
Web site: tm.org

REFERENCES

aan het Rot, M., D. S. Moskowitz, and S. N. Young. Exposure to bright light is associated with positive social interaction and good mood over short periods: A naturalistic study in mildly seasonal people. *Journal of Psychiatric Research* 42 (2008): 311—19.

Akbaraly, T. N. Diet rich in refined foods linked to increased risk for depression. *British Journal of Psychiatry* (2009).

Anon. Check your vitamin D intake to avoid multiple health consequences. Three 2008 studies link low vitamin D levels to depression, hip fractures, and increased risk of death. *Health News* 14 (2008): 9–10.

Babyak, M., J. A. Blumenthal, S. Herman, P. Khatri, M. Doraiswamy, K. Moore, W. E. Craighead, T. T. Baldewicz, and K. R. Krishnan. Exercise as a treatment for major depression: Maintenance of therapeutic benefit at 10 months. *Psychosomatic Medicine* 62 (2000): 633–38.

Barbour, K. A., T. M. Edenfield, and J. A. Blumenthal. Exercise as a treatment for depression and other psychiatric disorders: A review. *Journal of Cardiopulmonary Rehabilitation and Prevention* 27 (2007): 359–67.

Blair, S. N., M. J. LaMonte, and M. Z. Nichaman. The evolution of physical activity recommendations: How much is enough? *American Journal of Clinical Nutrition* 79 (2004): 913S–920S.

Blumenthal, J. A., M. A. Babyak, P. M. Doraiswamy, L. Watkins, B. M. Hoffman, K. A. Barbour, S. Herman, W. E. Craighead, A. L. Brosse, R. Waugh, A. Hinderliter, and A. Sherwood. Exercise and pharmacotherapy in the treatment of major depressive disorder. *Psychosomatic Medicine* 69 (2007): 587–96.

Bower, B. Slumber's unexplored landscape. *Science News* 156 (1999): 205.

Bricklin, Mark and Maggie Spilner, *Prevention's Practical Encyclopedia of Walking for Health.* Rodale, 1992

Byrd-Craven, J., D. C. Geary, A. J. Rose, and D. Ponzi. Co-ruminating increases stress hormone levels in women. *Hormones and Behavior* 53 (2008): 489–92.

Ciesla, J. A., and J. E. Roberts. Rumination, negative cognition, and their interactive effects on depressed mood. *Emotion* 7 (2007): 555–65.

Coan, J. A., and J. J. Allen. Frontal EEG asymmetry and the behavioral activation and inhibition systems. *Psychophysiology* 40 (2003): 106–14.

Dement, W. C. The promise of sleep. New York: Dell, 2000.

Demyttenaere, et al. Prevalence, severity, and unmet need for treatment of mental disorders in the World Health Organization World Mental Health Surveys. *Journal of the American Medical Association* 291 (21): 2581–90 (2004).

DeRubeis, R. J., D. Hollon, J. D. Amsterdam, R. C. Shelton, P. R. Young, R.M. Salomon, J. P. O'Reardon, M. L. Lovett, M. M. Gladis, L. L. Brown, and R. Gallop. Cognitive therapy versus medications in the treatment of moderate to severe depression. *Archives of General Psychiatry* 62 (2005): 409–16.

Dimidijan, S., S. D. Holon, K. S. Dobson, K. B. Schmaling, R. J. Kohlenberg, M. E. Addis, R. Gallop, J. B. McGlinchey, D. K. Markley, J. K. Gollan, D.C. Atkins, D. L. Dunner, and N. S. Jacobson. Randomized trial of behavioral activation, cognitive therapy, and antidepressant medication in the acute treatment of adults with major depression. *Journal of Consulting and Clinical Psychology* 74 (2006): 658–70.

Dworak, M., A. Waiter, D. Alfer, E. Stephan, W. Hollmann, and H. K. Struder. Increased slow wave sleep reduced stage 2 sleep in children depending on exercise intensity. *Sleep Medicine* 9 (2008): 266–72.

Egeland, J. A., and A. M. Hostetter. Amish study, I: Affective disorders among the Amish, 1976–1980. *American Journal of Psychiatry* 140 (1983): 56–61.

Emmons, R.A., and C. M. Shelton (2002). Gratitude and the science of positive psychology. In Snyder, C. R., and S. J. Lopez, (eds.). 2001. *Handbook of positive psychology* (pp. 459–71). Oxford: Oxford University Press.

Fried, Robert. The psychology and physiology of breathing. 1991. New York: Plenum Press.

Hallahan, B., J. R. Hibbeln, J. M. Davis, and M. R. Garland. Omega-3 fatty acid supplementation in patients with recurrent self-harm. Single-centre double-blind randomised controlled trial. *British Journal of Psychiatry* 190 (2007): 118–22.

Hendricks, PhD, Gay. *Conscious Breathing.* Bantam Books, 1995.

Henriques, J. B., and R. J. Davidson. Left frontal hypoactivation in depression. *Journal of Abnormal Psychology* 100 (1991): 535–45.

Holick, M. F. Vitamin D status: Measurement, interpretation, and clinical application. *Annals of Epidemiology* 19 (2009): 73–78.

Kaminoff, Leslie. What yoga therapists should know about the anatomy of breathing. *International Journal of Yoga Therapy* 16 (2006): 66–77.

Kessler, R. C., P. Berglund, O. Demler, R. Jin, and E. E. Walters. Lifetime prevalence and age-of-onset distributions of DSM-IV disorders in the national comorbidity survey replication. *Archives of General Psychiatry* 62 (2005): 593–602.

Khan, A., R. M. Leventhal, S. R. Khan, and W. A. Brown. Severity of depression and response to antidepressants and placebo: An analysis of the Food and Drug Administration Database. *Journal of Clinical Psychopharmacology* 22: 40–45.

Kirsch, I., T. J. Moore, A. Scoboria, and S. S. Nicholls. The emperor's new drugs: An analysis of antidepressant medication data submitted to the U.S. Food and Drug Administration. *Prevention & Treatment* 5, article 23 (2002).

Knapen, J., E. Sommerijns, D. Vancampfort, P. Sienaert, G. Pieters, P. Haake, M. Probst, and J. Peuskens. State anxiety and subjective well-being responses to acute bouts of aerobic exercise in patients with depressive and anxiety disorders. *British Journal of Sports Medicine* (2008).

Lovett, R. Coffee: The demon drink? *New Scientist* 2518 (2005).

Marshall, T. G. Vitamin D discovery outpaces FDA decision making. *Bioessays* 30 (2008): 173–82.

McPherson, J. M., L. Smith-Lovin, and M. B. Brashears. Social isolation in America: changes in core discussion networks over two decades. *American Sociological Review* 71 (2006): 353–75.

Miller, A. H., V. Maletic, and C. L. Raison. Inflammation and its discontents: The role of cytokines in the pathophysiology of major depression. *Biological Psychiatry* (2009).

Miller, K. B., B. Yost, A. Flaherty, M. M. Hillemeier, G. A. Chase, C. S. Weisman, and A. M. Dyer. Health status, health conditions, and health behaviors among Amish women: Results from the Central Pennsylvania Women's Health Study (CePAWHS). *Women's Health Issues* 17 (2007): 162–71.

Moulds, M. L., E. Kandris, S. Starr, and A. C. Wong. The relationship between rumination, avoidance and depression in a non-clinical sample. *Behavioral Research and Therapy* 45 (2007): 251–61.

Mynors-Wallis, L., I. Davies, A. Gray, F. Barbour, and D. Gath. A randomised controlled trial and cost analysis of problem-solving treatment for emotional disorders given by community nurses in primary care. *British Journal of Psychiatry* 170 (1997): 113–19.

National Sleep Foundation. 2008 Sleep in America Poll. sleepfoundation.org.

Nolen-Hoeksema, S., B. E. Wisco, and S. Lyubomirsky. Rethinking rumination. *Perspectives on Psychological Science* 3 (2008): 400–424.

Ogden, C. L., M. D. Carroll, L. R. Curtin, M. A. McDowell, C. J. Tabak, and K. M. Flegal. Prevalence of overweight and obesity in the United States, 1999–2004. *Journal of the American Medical Association* 295 (2006): 1549–55.

Pargament, K. I., McCullough, M. E., and Thoresen, C. E. 2000. The frontier of forgiveness: Seven directions for psychological study and practice. In M. E. McCullough, K. I. Pargament, and C. E. Thoresen (eds.). 2001. Forgiveness: Theory, research, and practice (pp. 299–319). New York: Guilford Press.

Parker, G. B., J. Crawford, and D. Hadzi-Pavlovic. Quantified superiority of cognitive behaviour and therapy to antidepressant drugs: A challenge to an earlier meta-analysis. *Acta Psychiatrica Scandinavica* 118 (2008): 91–97.

Paykel, E. S. Cognitive-behavioral therapy is better than antidepressants at preventing relapse. *Journal of Neuropsychopharmacology* (2006).

Peet, M. International variations in the outcome of schizophrenia and the prevalence of depression in relation to national dietary practices: An ecological analysis. *British Journal of Psychiatry* 284 (2004): 404–8.

Penedo, F. J., and J. R. Dahn. Exercise and well-being: A review of mental and psychological health benefits associated with physical activity. *Current Opinion in Psychiatry* 18 (2005): 189–93.

Prevention. Best Prescription for Your Back. December 2001.

Prevention. *"Core" Secret to a Better Body.* April 2002.

Putnam, R. D. 2000. *Bowling alone: The collapse and revival of American community.* New York: Simon & Schuster.

Sánchez-Villegas, A. Mediterranean diet may cut depression risk: Depression risk 30% lower in those who ate mediterranean diet. *Archives of General Psychiatry* October 2009.

Sears, B. 2002. The omega Rx zone: The miracle of the new high-dose fish oil. New York: Collins Living.

Seligman, M. Why is there so much depression today? The waxing of the individual and the waning of the commons. In Rex Ingram (ed.). 1990. *Contemporary psychological approaches to depression* (pp. 1–9). New York: Plenum.

Seligman, M. E., T. A. Steen, N. Park, and C. Peterson. 2005. Positive psychology progress: Empirical validation of interventions. *American Psychologist* 60: 410–21.

Spilner, Maggie, *Prevention's Complete Book of Walking.* Rodale, 2000.

Stagnitti, M. N. *Statistical brief #206: Antidepressants prescribed by medical doctors in office based and outpatient settings by specialty for the U.S. civilian noninstitutionalized population, 2002 and 2005.* Agency for Healthcare Research and Quality: Medical Expenditure Panel Survey, June 2008.

Thase, M. E. Correlates and consequences of chronic insomnia. *General Hospital Psychiatry* 2 (2005): 100–112.

U.S. Department of Health and Human Services. *Physical activity and health: A report of the Surgeon General.* Atlanta: U.S. Department of Health and Human Services, Centers for Disease Control and Prevention National Center for Chronic Disease Prevention and Health Promotion, 1999.

Weissman, M. M., R. C. Bland, G. J. Canino, C. Faravelli, S. Greenwald, H. G. Hwu, P. R. Joyce, E. G. Kara, C. K. Lee, J. Lellouch, J. P. Lépine, S. C. Newman, M. Rubio-Stipec, J. E. Wells, P. J. Wickramaratne, H. Wittchen, and E. K. Yeh. Cross-national epidemiology of major depression and bipolar disorder. *Journal of the American Medical Association* 276 (1996): 293–99.

Women's Health, "Walk off 10, 25, even 50 pounds" Rodale, 2002.

♥ ACKNOWLEDGMENTS

It took a village to create this book.

I am most grateful to Maria Rodale, CEO of Rodale Inc. for helping to bring the project to life. Maria is a true visionary, whose passion for promoting health and the health of our planet is helping to change the world. Kudos to Karen Rinaldi, David Kang, Rick Chillot, and all the dedicated and talented staff at Rodale whose efforts made this book a reality. Big thanks to my editor extraordinaire, Julie Will, whose word-crafting genius helped make the final version engaging and accessible.

Kim Witherspoon, my fabulous agent, and Julie Schilder, her skillful associate, at Inkwell Management gave me wise counsel and on-going education about the subtleties of book publishing.

Over the past 25 years, Tom Yeomans has been a wise, caring teacher, mentor, colleague, and friend. His guidance at the inception of the book and his thoughtful review of the manuscript were invaluable.

I owe a debt of gratitude to Richard Billow and Gordon Derner, my graduate-school mentors, who nurtured my development as a psychotherapist and researcher.

My understanding of an integrative, mind-body approach to healing was fortified through collaboration with my brilliant friend and colleague, Jesse Stoff. With Jesse and our wonderful colleagues at Solstice, Doug Astion, Amanda Newman, Colleen Stoff, Ruth Finzer, Sarah and Neil Orenstein, and Diane Rossman, I experienced the powerful healing synergy of a collaborative, like-minded multidisciplinary team.

I want to thank the many people at Canyon Ranch who have supported me over the past eighteen years. I am forever grateful to Enid and Mel Zuckerman for their vision and dedication to creating an extraordinary healing environment. Special thanks to Jerry Cohen and Gary Frost for their strong leadership and continual support.

I have been blessed to work with a talented group of colleagues at Canyon Ranch. Dan Baker generously shared his knowledge, guidance, and enthusiasm through our years of collaboration. Demie Stathoplos and Bill Swann provided administrative support for my work and enthusiastic encouragement for my writing. Every day I appreciate Emilie Goudey for her enlightened leadership and unwavering support.

I have been fortunate to work with an amazing administrative staff at Canyon Ranch who support me, my fellow practitioners and our guests: Regina Scolforo, Tina McIntyre, Cathryn Duffy, Michele Wojtkowski, Christina Leonard , Shelly Lester, Joanne Cimini, Anne Feltmate, Mary Johnson, Ginny Severance and Brenda Crane. I am grateful to our health program staff who oversee the various components of our guests' treatment, including Cindy Midgley, Wendy Bartsch, Joanne Leavitt, Cathy Cardell, Judy Burt, Lorna Gayle, and Kaye Bottega.

I have been very fortunate to collaborate with and learn from an extraordinary group of integrative physicians at Canyon Ranch, including Mark Liponis, Cindy Geyer, Tereza Hubkova, Nina Molin, and Kevin Murray. Our patients have benefitted greatly from their rare ability to integrate the best of traditional and complementary medical approaches.

I have learned most from my patients, who have allowed me to accompany them on their healing journey. I owe a special debt of gratitude to all those who so generously agreed to share their stories to help others.

Several of my friends and colleagues from the Association for the Advancement and Study of Clinical Hypnosis provided valuable ideas for making the book practical and accessible, including Deb Hewitt, Wayne Carpenter, George Abbott, Ralph Cohen, Peggy Braun, Teresa Gentile, Chris Morrison, Rorry Zahourek, Glenn Fagen, Amy Kahn, Tiana Mirapae, Sue James, and Jon Kolodin.

I am much indebted to my colleagues in the Life Management Department at Canyon Ranch who shared their encouragement, feedback, and expertise. Janet Doucette lent her extraordinary talents to researching and preparing content for several chapters of the book. Diane Dillon provided insightful feedback and good-natured encouragement as the project moved into its final stages. Over the years, Melanie Masdea, Eileen Lawlor, Marcia Bernstein, Kristine Huffman, Sharon Fay and Tom Plunkett shared their insights into emotional healing that have informed my work and my thinking.

My friend, Leslie Kaminoff, an international expert on the anatomy and physiology of yoga, provided invaluable feedback on the breathing chapter. Mark Hyman, friend and colleague, one of the world's leading authorities on functional medicine, gave extensive input into the chapter on nutrition and nutritional supplements. Theta Pattison, friend, colleague, and gifted physician, generously provided her enthusiasm, encouragement, and editorial review of the entire manuscript, with extraordinary clarity and perceptiveness.

Several other friends and colleagues provided important feedback and advice, including Belisa Vranich, Maria Sirois, Abby Seixas, Mark Horowitz, Warren Spielberg, and Michael Thompson.

Many friends supported me with their interest and encouragement, including Joanne O'Neil, Ingrid Willgren, Michele Lacroix, Catherine and Bill Shields, Steve and Kaya Kauffman, Larry Wallach, Anna Legene, Jackie and Alan Roland, Mitch Gurfield, Michael Marcus, George Mayer, and Charlie Ferris. Special thanks to Susan Murphy and Ed Ritz for generously offering their loft when I needed a quiet space to write.

Several members of my family had a hand in this book. My parents, Anita and Herb Rossman, reviewed the chapter detailing our family's experience with depression and corrected my imprecise recollection of what actually happened 50 years ago. I owe this work and much more to their love and their example of loving commitment to what truly matters. My unstoppable sister, Tammi Benjamin, has always been there to laugh, empathize, and dream big dreams with me. My big-hearted, absolutely dependable brother, Steve, is the one I've turned to for practical advice on just about everything. Thanks to my mother-in-law, Phyllis Braverman, for allowing me to share her story, and to my father-in-law, Richard Braverman, for his enthusiastic, on-going interest in my work.

My children, Gabriel and Grace, deserve special thanks for their patience and for the valuable help they provided. Gabriel researched material for the exercise chapters, and Grace contributed her formidable literary talent to certain passages of the text.

My deepest gratitude is to my wife, Diane. A gifted therapist and magnificent writer, she critiqued and revised numerous drafts of the manuscript. Her infinite love, understanding and encouragement sustained me through the journey. Her wisdom and sensibility are present in every page of this page of this book.

INDEX

Underscored page references indicate charts.